IQ WORKOUT

BRAINTRAINING PUZZLES

IQ WORKOUT

BRAINTRAINING PUZZLES

with over 180 puzzles

ARCTURUS

ARCTURUS

This edition published in 2011 by Arcturus Publishing Limited
26/27 Bickels Yard, 151–153 Bermondsey Street,
London SE1 3HA

ISBN: 978-1-84837-652-6
AD001433EN

Printed in China

CONTENTS

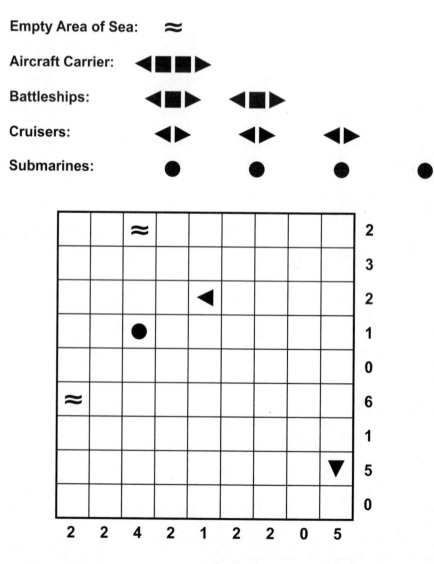

BATTLESHIPS

Can you place the vessels into the diagram? Some parts of vessels or sea squares have already been filled in. A number to the right or below a row or column refers to the number of occupied squares in that row or column.

Any vessel may be positioned horizontally or vertically, but no part of a vessel touches part of any other vessel, either horizontally, vertically or diagonally.

Empty Area of Sea: ≈

Aircraft Carrier: ◀■■▶

Battleships: ◀■▶   ◀■▶

Cruisers: ◀▶   ◀▶   ◀▶

Submarines: ●   ●   ●   ●

ELIMINATOR

2

Every oval shape contains a different letter of the alphabet from A to K inclusive. Use the clues to determine their locations. Reference in the clues to 'due' means in any location along the same horizontal or vertical line.

1 C is due east of H, which is due south of B.

2 F is due west of D, which is due south of E.

3 I is due east of F, which is due north of H.

4 G is due west of A, which is due north of I.

5 J is due south of K.

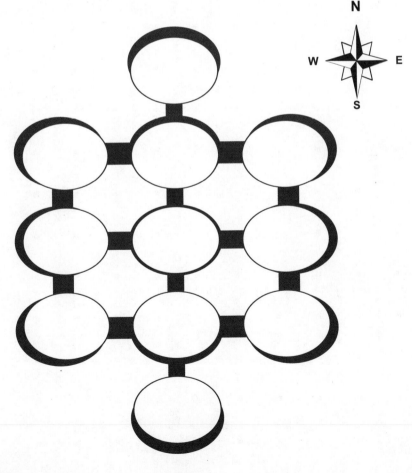

SLITHERLINK

Draw a single continuous loop, by connecting the dots. No line may cross the path of another.

The figure inside each set of any four surrounding dots indicates the total number of surrounding lines.

PIECEWORK

Place all twelve of the pieces into the grid. Any may be rotated or flipped over, but none may touch another, not even diagonally.

The numbers outside the grid refer to the number of consecutive black squares; and each block is separated from the others by at least one white square. For instance, '3 2' could refer to a row with none, one or more white squares, then three black squares, then at least one white square, then two more black squares, followed by any number of white squares.

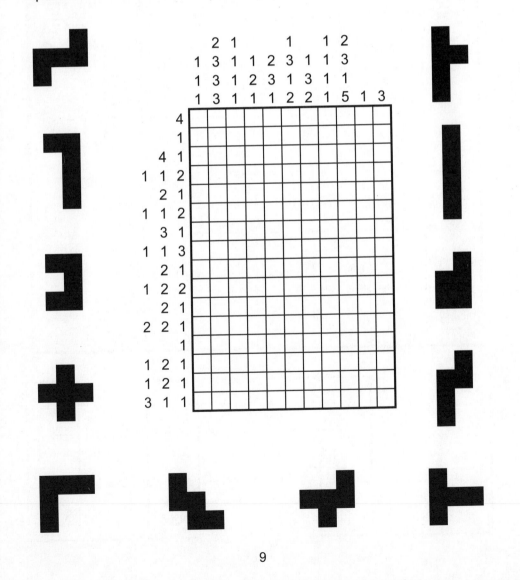

WHERE THE L?

Twelve L-shapes (three pieces of each of the four kinds shown below) need to be inserted in the grid and each L has one hole in it.

Any piece may be turned or flipped over before being put in the grid. No pieces of the same kind touch, even at a corner. The pieces fit together so well that you cannot see any spaces between them; only the holes show. Can you tell where the Ls are?

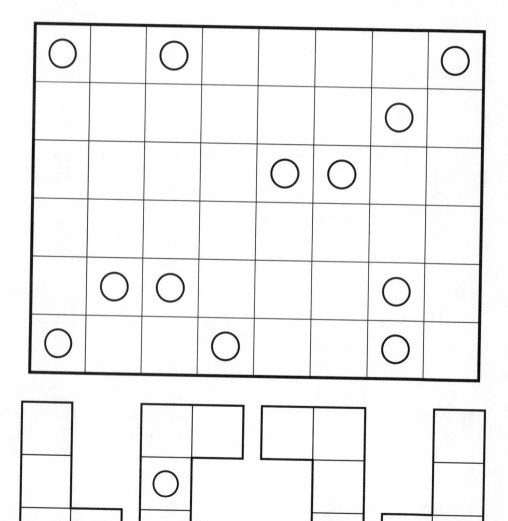

In this puzzle, an amateur coin collector has been out with his metal detector, searching for booty. He didn't have time to dig up all the coins he found, so has made a grid map, showing their locations, in the hope that if he loses the map, at least no-one else will understand it... However, he didn't count on YOU coming across the strange grid (as seen here). Will you be able to discover the correct number of coins and their precise locations?

Those squares containing numbers are empty, but where a number appears in a square, it indicates how many coins are located in the squares (up to a maximum of eight) surrounding the numbered one, touching it at any corner or side. There is only one coin in any individual square.

Place a circle into every square containing a coin.

	1		1			0	
1		2		2			
				1			0
		4				2	
	4						
0					1	3	
		1			1		
	3		1			3	
				1	1	2	2
	5						
			0				3
	3				3		

BOX CLEVER

When the box below is folded to form a cube, just one of the five options (A, B, C, D or E) can be produced. Which?

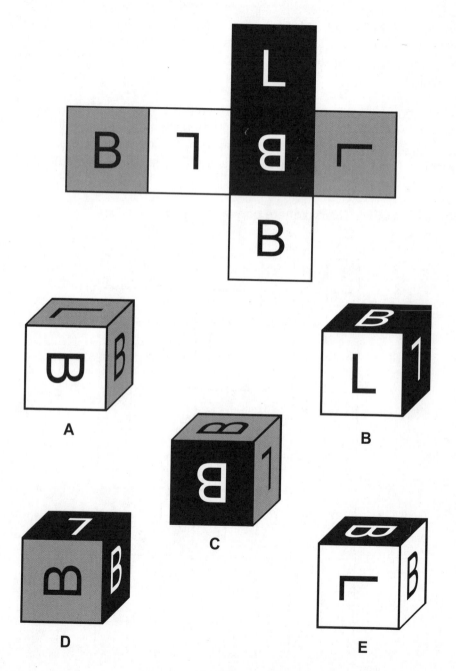

SYMBOLISM

Each of these squares should contain one or more symbols from the numbered square to the left of its particular horizontal row, plus one or more symbols from the lettered square above its particular vertical column. However, one square doesn't follow this rule. Which is the odd one out?

	A	B	C	D	E	F
	◄ ₪	⅄ $	‡ »	♦ #	♪ ±	Σ 🏛
1 ≠ Π	Π ◄ ₪	$ ≠ Π	» ‡ Π ≠	♦ # ≠	Π ♪	≠ 🏛 Π
2 ♠ Θ	Θ ₪ ♠	⅄ $ Θ	‡ » Θ	♠ # ♦	Θ ± ♪	Σ 🏛 Θ
3 • ►	₪ ◄ •	► • ⅄ $	‡ ► • »	♦ • #	± ♪ •	• Σ ►
4 Ω §	◄ § Ω	§ Ω $	» § Ω ‡	§ # Ω	Ω ♪	§ Ω
5 Δ ♥	♥ ◄ ₪	$ ⅄ Δ ♥	Δ » ♥ ‡	# Δ ♥	♥ Δ ±	Σ ♥ Δ
6 ▲ †	◄ † ◄ ▲	⅄ † ▲ $	▲ » †	# † ♦	▲ † ± ♪	▲ 🏛 Σ †
7 ▼ Π	₪ Π ▼ ◄	⅄ ▼ $	Π ‡ ▼	♦ # Π	Π ♪ ±	▼ Σ Π

TILE TWISTER

Place the eight tiles into the puzzle grid so that all adjacent numbers on each tile match up. Tiles may be rotated through 360 degrees, but none may be flipped over.

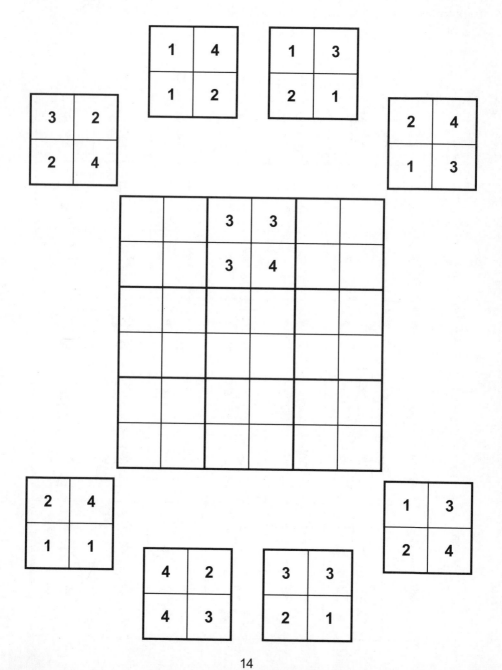

Every row and column of this grid should contain one each of the letters A, B, C, D, E and F. In addition, each of the six shapes (marked by thicker lines) should also contain one each of the letters A, B, C, D, E and F. Can you complete the grid?

A   B   C   D   E   F

		B		A	
		C			
		F			
			E		D
				F	

BATTLESHIPS

Can you place the vessels into the diagram? Some parts of vessels or sea squares have already been filled in. A number to the right or below a row or column refers to the number of occupied squares in that row or column.

Any vessel may be positioned horizontally or vertically, but no part of a vessel touches part of any other vessel, either horizontally, vertically or diagonally.

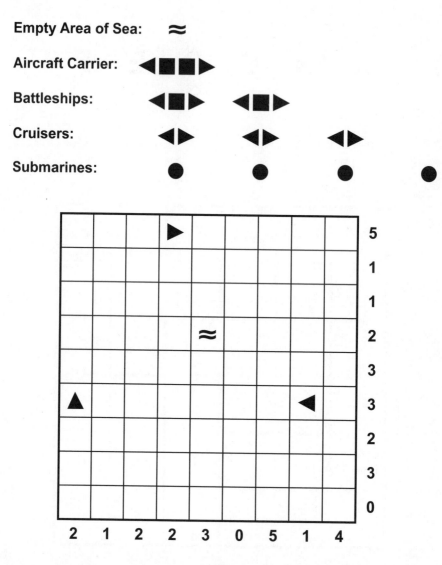

Every oval shape contains a different letter of the alphabet from A to K inclusive. Use the clues to determine their locations. Reference in the clues to 'due' means in any location along the same horizontal or vertical line.

1   A is both due west of B and due south of D, which is due north of C.

2   H is due west of G, which is due south of A.

3   F is due west of A, which is due north of E.

4   K is due south of I, which is due east of C.

5   F is due south of J.

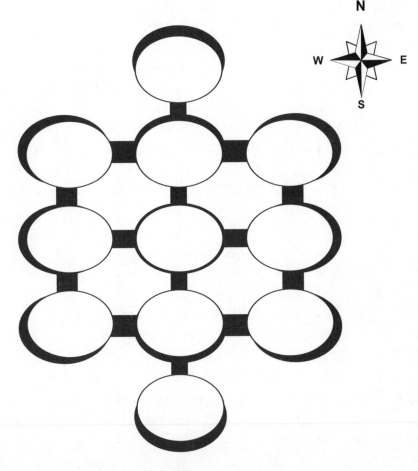

SLITHERLINK

Draw a single continuous loop, by connecting the dots. No line may cross the path of another.

The figure inside each set of any four surrounding dots indicates the total number of surrounding lines.

Place all twelve of the pieces into the grid. Any may be rotated or flipped over, but none may touch another, not even diagonally.

The numbers outside the grid refer to the number of consecutive black squares; and each block is separated from the others by at least one white square. For instance, '3 2' could refer to a row with none, one or more white squares, then three black squares, then at least one white square, then two more black squares, followed by any number of white squares.

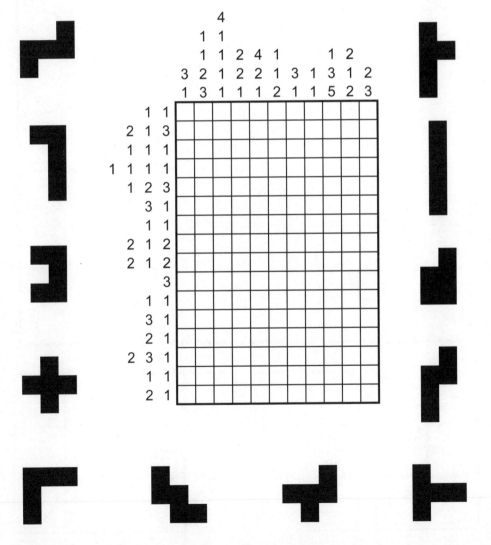

WHERE THE L?

Twelve L-shapes (three pieces of each of the four kinds shown below) need to be inserted in the grid and each L has one hole in it.

Any piece may be turned or flipped over before being put in the grid. No pieces of the same kind touch, even at a corner. The pieces fit together so well that you cannot see any spaces between them; only the holes show. Can you tell where the Ls are?

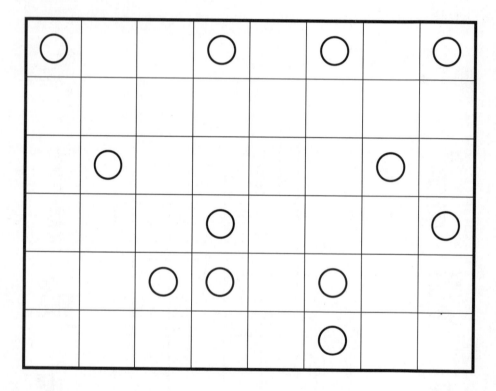

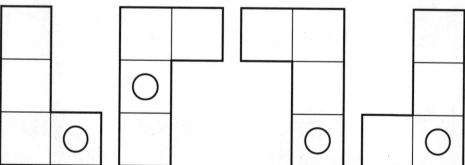

In this puzzle, an amateur coin collector has been out with his metal detector, searching for booty. He didn't have time to dig up all the coins he found, so has made a grid map, showing their locations, in the hope that if he loses the map, at least no-one else will understand it... However, he didn't count on YOU coming across the strange grid (as seen here). Will you be able to discover the correct number of coins and their precise locations?

Those squares containing numbers are empty, but where a number appears in a square, it indicates how many coins are located in the squares (up to a maximum of eight) surrounding the numbered one, touching it at any corner or side. There is only one coin in any individual square.

Place a circle into every square containing a coin.

	3		2				2
		4	3			3	
4		3			2		3
						2	
2				0			
		4					
	1				2		1
2			4				1
				1	0		
			3			1	0
	3	3	3			1	
	1		2				

BOX CLEVER

When the box below is folded to form a cube, just one of the five options (A, B, C, D or E) can be produced. Which?

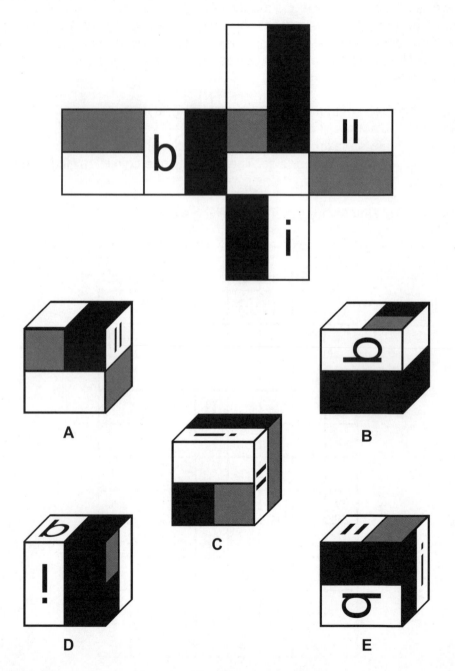

A

B

C

D

E

Each of these squares should contain one or more symbols from the numbered square to the left of its particular horizontal row, plus one or more symbols from the lettered square above its particular vertical column. However, one square doesn't follow this rule. Which is the odd one out?

	A	B	C	D	E	F
	◄ ¶	‡ ☼	♣ ¿	♦ #	♪ ≈	Σ $
1	E π	E ◄ ¶ π	E ‡ π	¿ E ♣	π E #♦	π ♪ ≈	π $ E Σ
2	♠ &	♠ ¶ ◄&	& ☼ ‡	♠ ¿ ♣&	♦ & ♠	≈& ♪ ♠	♠ $ &
3	6 ►	¶ 6	☼ ► 6	¿ 6 ♣	6 ► ♦	► ≈ 6 ♪	$ 6 ►
4	ß §	§ ß ¶ ◄	☼‡ § ß	ß ♣ ¿ §	♦ § #	§ ≈ ß ♪	Σ ß $
5	▲ ♥	◄ ▲ ♥	▲ ‡ ☼	♥ ▲ ¿	♥ ♦ ▲	≈ ▲ ♦	Σ $ ♥
6	▼ ♫	¶ ▼ ◄ ♫	‡ ♪ ▼	¿ ▼ ♫	♫ ▼ ♦	≈ ♪ ▼ ♫	$ ♫ ▼
7	Δ φ	φ Δ ◄	☼ Δ φ	♣ φ Δ	# ♦ φ	Δ ♪ φ	$ Δ φ

23

TILE TWISTER

Place the eight tiles into the puzzle grid so that all adjacent numbers on each tile match up. Tiles may be rotated through 360 degrees, but none may be flipped over.

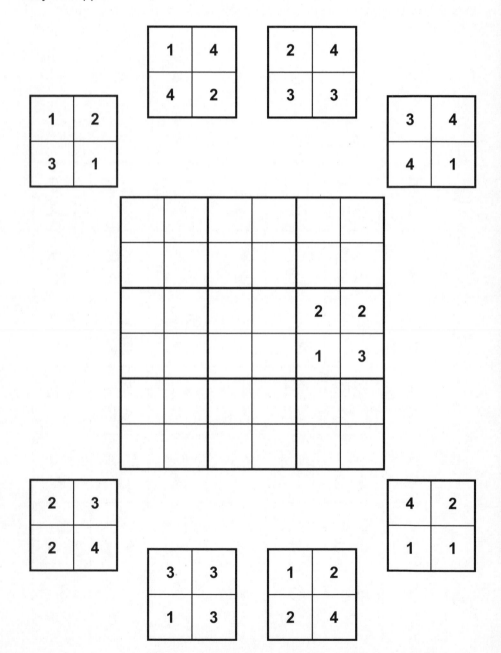

LOGI-6

Every row and column of this grid should contain one each of the letters A, B, C, D, E and F. In addition, each of the six shapes (marked by thicker lines) should also contain one each of the letters A, B, C, D, E and F. Can you complete the grid?

A B C D E F

BATTLESHIPS

Can you place the vessels into the diagram? Some parts of vessels or sea squares have already been filled in. A number to the right or below a row or column refers to the number of occupied squares in that row or column.

Any vessel may be positioned horizontally or vertically, but no part of a vessel touches part of any other vessel, either horizontally, vertically or diagonally.

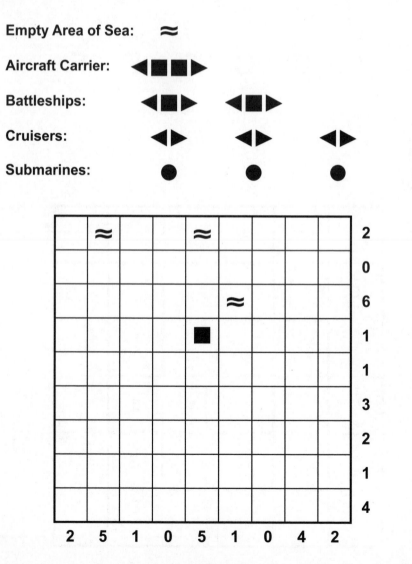

ELIMINATOR

Every oval shape contains a different letter of the alphabet from A to K inclusive. Use the clues to determine their locations. Reference in the clues to 'due' means in any location along the same horizontal or vertical line.

1　G is due north of J, which is due west of F.
2　H is due south of I, which is due west of B.
3　D is due east of E, which is next to and north of C.
4　A is both further west and further north than K.
5　K is both further north and further east than C.
6　C is both further south and further east than H.
7　A is further west than G.

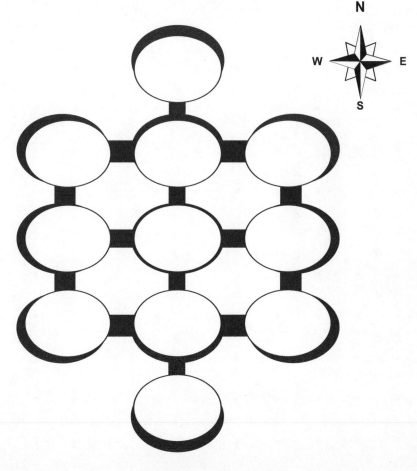

SLITHERLINK

Draw a single continuous loop, by connecting the dots. No line may cross the path of another.

The figure inside each set of any four surrounding dots indicates the total number of surrounding lines.

PIECEWORK

Place all twelve of the pieces into the grid. Any may be rotated or flipped over, but none may touch another, not even diagonally.

The numbers outside the grid refer to the number of consecutive black squares; and each block is separated from the others by at least one white square. For instance, '3 2' could refer to a row with none, one or more white squares, then three black squares, then at least one white square, then two more black squares, followed by any number of white squares.

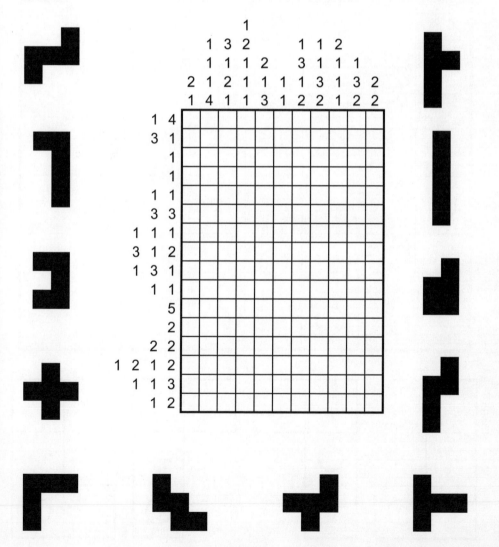

WHERE THE L?

Twelve L-shapes (three pieces of each of the four kinds shown below) need to be inserted in the grid and each L has one hole in it.

Any piece may be turned or flipped over before being put in the grid. No pieces of the same kind touch, even at a corner. The pieces fit together so well that you cannot see any spaces between them; only the holes show. Can you tell where the Ls are?

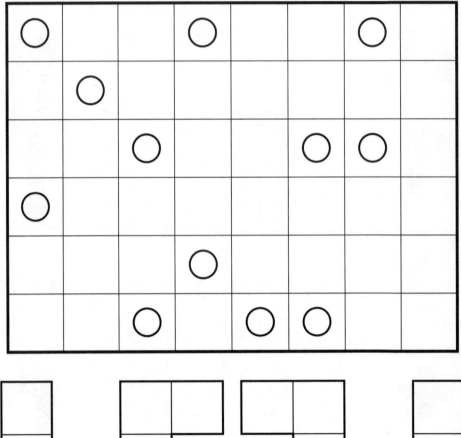

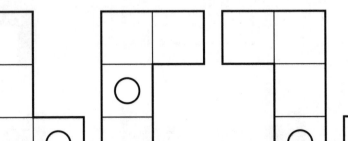

In this puzzle, an amateur coin collector has been out with his metal detector, searching for booty. He didn't have time to dig up all the coins he found, so has made a grid map, showing their locations, in the hope that if he loses the map, at least no-one else will understand it... However, he didn't count on YOU coming across the strange grid (as seen here). Will you be able to discover the correct number of coins and their precise locations?

Those squares containing numbers are empty, but where a number appears in a square, it indicates how many coins are located in the squares (up to a maximum of eight) surrounding the numbered one, touching it at any corner or side. There is only one coin in any individual square.

Place a circle into every square containing a coin.

							1
	0			0			
1			0		1	3	3
		2		3			
	2				2		2
		4	4			1	
					0		
	3			2			
	5	3				3	
		1			3	4	
	3			2			

BOX CLEVER

When the box below is folded to form a cube, just one of the five options (A, B, C, D or E) can be produced. Which?

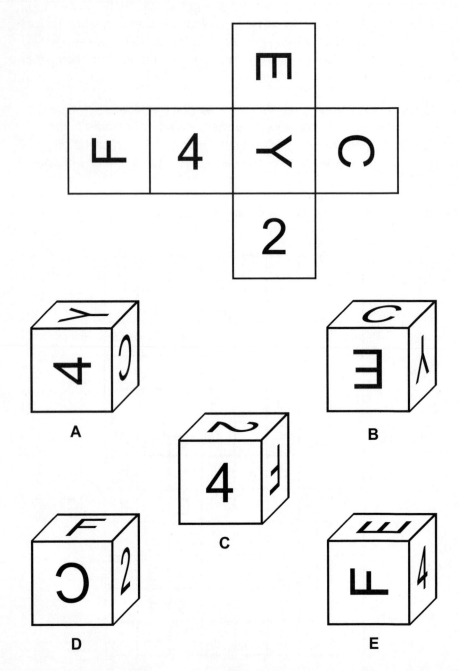

Each of these squares should contain one or more symbols from the numbered square to the left of its particular horizontal row, plus one or more symbols from the lettered square above its particular vertical column. However, one square doesn't follow this rule. Which is the odd one out?

	A	B	C	D	E	F
	◄ H	G $	M ¿	◆ #	♪ ¶	Σ P
1 8 π	◄ 8 π	8 $ G	π M 8	# 8 π	8 ¶ π ♪	Σ P π
2 F ß	ß ◄ H	F ß $	ß M F	F ◆ #	¶ ß F	F ß Σ
3 £ ►	◄ ► £	£ ► G	M ► ¿	► ◆ #	♪ £ ¶	P ►
4 Ω §	Ω H	G Ω § $	¿ M §	◆ # Ω	¶ Ω §	§ P Σ
5 Z 4	Z H	$ 4 G	4 Z ¿	◆ Z # 4	♪ 4	P Z Σ
6 ▲ B	▲ H ◄	▲ B $ G	M ¿	◆ B ▲	♪ ▲ B ¶	B Σ P
7 ▼ φ	◄ ▼ φ H	▼ $ φ	¿ M ▼	# ◆ ▼	φ ♪ ▼	P ▼ Σ φ

TILE TWISTER

Place the eight tiles into the puzzle grid so that all adjacent numbers on each tile match up. Tiles may be rotated through 360 degrees, but none may be flipped over.

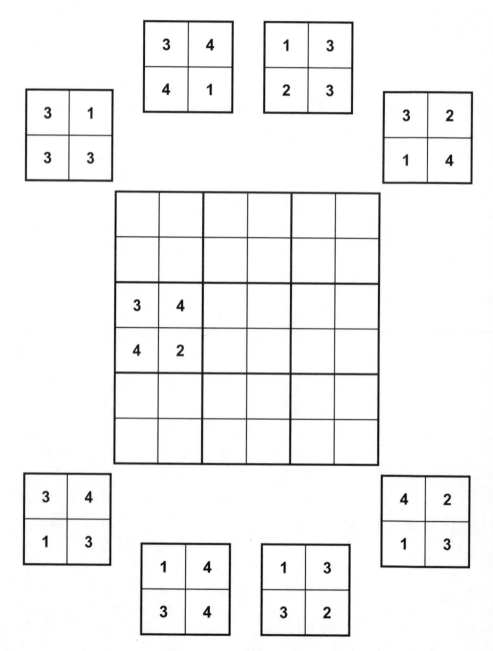

Every row and column of this grid should contain one each of the letters A, B, C, D, E and F. In addition, each of the six shapes (marked by thicker lines) should also contain one each of the letters A, B, C, D, E and F. Can you complete the grid?

A   B   C   D   E   F

C				B	A
			D		
E					
		F			
				C	

BATTLESHIPS

Can you place the vessels into the diagram? Some parts of vessels or sea squares have already been filled in. A number to the right or below a row or column refers to the number of occupied squares in that row or column.

Any vessel may be positioned horizontally or vertically, but no part of a vessel touches part of any other vessel, either horizontally, vertically or diagonally.

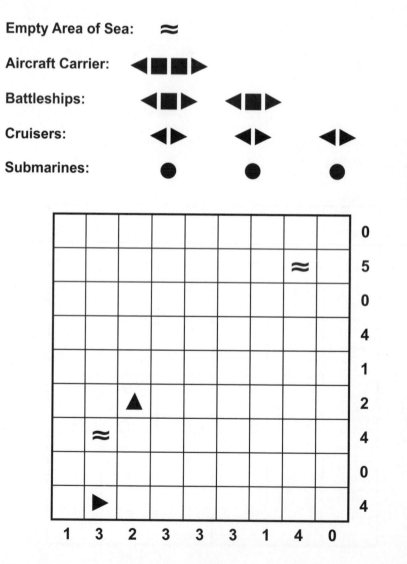

Every oval shape contains a different letter of the alphabet from A to K inclusive. Use the clues to determine their locations. Reference in the clues to 'due' means in any location along the same horizontal or vertical line.

1 B is next to and west of I, which is due north of H.
2 G is next to and west of A, which is due north of D.
3 E is next to and north of J, which is further north than A.
4 F is next to and north of K, which is next to and west of C.
5 F is both further north and further east than E.

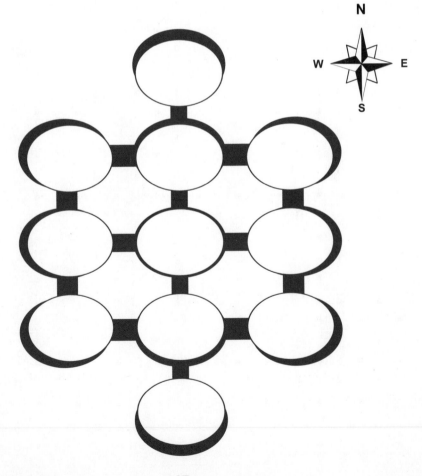

SLITHERLINK

Draw a single continuous loop, by connecting the dots. No line may cross the path of another.

The figure inside each set of any four surrounding dots indicates the total number of surrounding lines.

Place all twelve of the pieces into the grid. Any may be rotated or flipped over, but none may touch another, not even diagonally.

The numbers outside the grid refer to the number of consecutive black squares; and each block is separated from the others by at least one white square. For instance, '3 2' could refer to a row with none, one or more white squares, then three black squares, then at least one white square, then two more black squares, followed by any number of white squares.

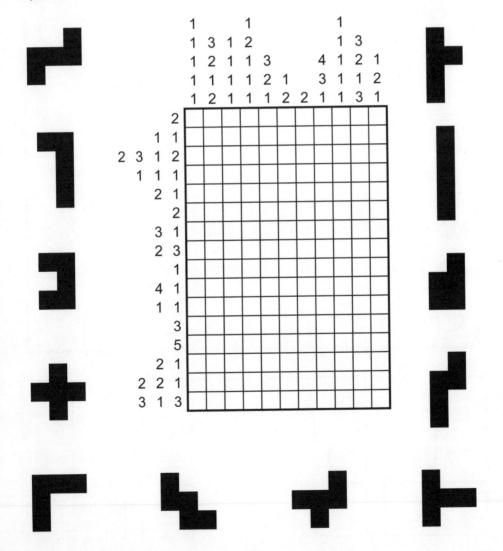

WHERE THE L?

Twelve L-shapes (three pieces of each of the four kinds shown below) need to be inserted in the grid and each L has one hole in it.

Any piece may be turned or flipped over before being put in the grid. No pieces of the same kind touch, even at a corner. The pieces fit together so well that you cannot see any spaces between them; only the holes show. Can you tell where the Ls are?

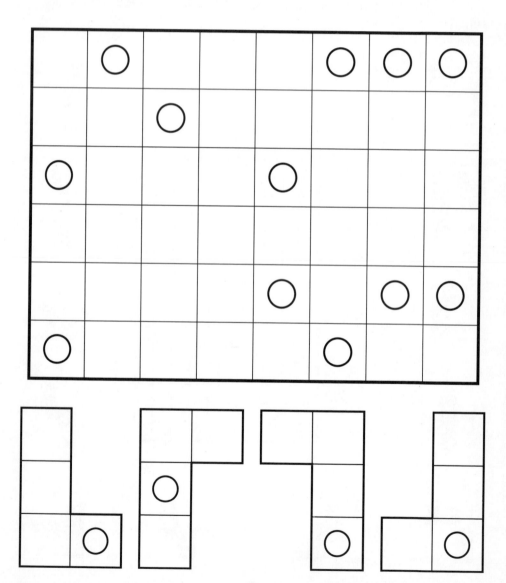

In this puzzle, an amateur coin collector has been out with his metal detector, searching for booty. He didn't have time to dig up all the coins he found, so has made a grid map, showing their locations, in the hope that if he loses the map, at least no-one else will understand it... However, he didn't count on YOU coming across the strange grid (as seen here). Will you be able to discover the correct number of coins and their precise locations?

Those squares containing numbers are empty, but where a number appears in a square, it indicates how many coins are located in the squares (up to a maximum of eight) surrounding the numbered one, touching it at any corner or side. There is only one coin in any individual square.

Place a circle into every square containing a coin.

0			2		2		
				3			2
		2					
	3		1		2	4	3
2		3	2				
			2	2	2	4	
	3	3	2			4	
2	2				2		
1		4			1		1
			2				
	2			1	1	1	

BOX CLEVER

When the box below is folded to form a cube, just one of the five options (A, B, C, D or E) can be produced. Which?

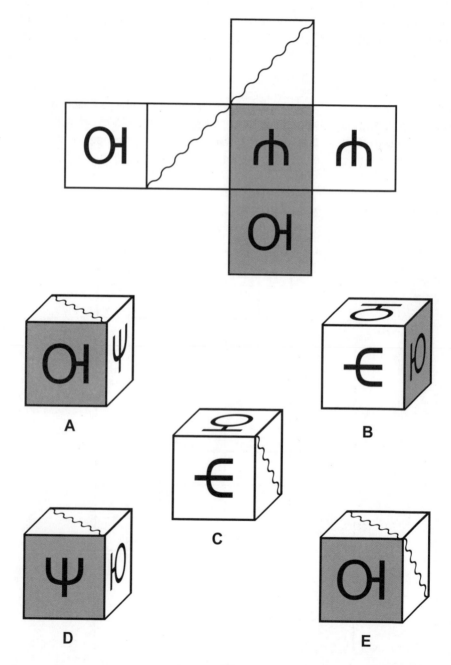

A

B

C

D

E

Each of these squares should contain one or more symbols from the numbered square to the left of its particular horizontal row, plus one or more symbols from the lettered square above its particular vertical column. However, one square doesn't follow this rule. Which is the odd one out?

	A	B	C	D	E	F
	R ≈	L $	‡ ¿	N #	♪ 3	1 ☼
1 ∩ T	RT ≈∩	∩ $ T	∩ ‡ ¿	N T∩	∩ T♪	1T ☼
2 ♠ 7	R ♠7	♠ 7L	7 ♠‡	#♠ N	♪ ♠3	♠1 7☼
3 Q ▶	≈R ▶	▶L Q$	‡ Q¿	Q# N	▶ Q♪	▶Q ☼
4 F §	R F	§ L$	§ ¿	N §	F♪	1 ☼§
5 G ♥	≈G R	G$ L♥	‡ ¿G	♥N #	♪ 3♥	G1 ♥
6 8 ♪	R ♪≈	$L ♪8	¿ ♪	8 N#	♪8 ♪	8 ☼
7 ▼ 9	R ≈▼	9L ▼	▼‡ ¿	#9 N▼	♪ 3	91 ☼

TILE TWISTER

Place the eight tiles into the puzzle grid so that all adjacent numbers on each tile match up. Tiles may be rotated through 360 degrees, but none may be flipped over.

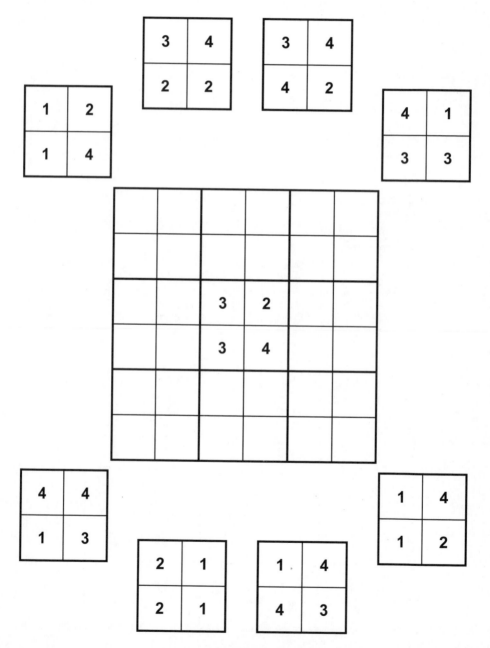

Every row and column of this grid should contain one each of the letters A, B, C, D, E and F. In addition, each of the six shapes (marked by thicker lines) should also contain one each of the letters A, B, C, D, E and F. Can you complete the grid?

A B C D E F

			C	B	A
	A				
				D	
E					
			F		

BATTLESHIPS

Can you place the vessels into the diagram? Some parts of vessels or sea squares have already been filled in. A number to the right or below a row or column refers to the number of occupied squares in that row or column.

Any vessel may be positioned horizontally or vertically, but no part of a vessel touches part of any other vessel, either horizontally, vertically or diagonally.

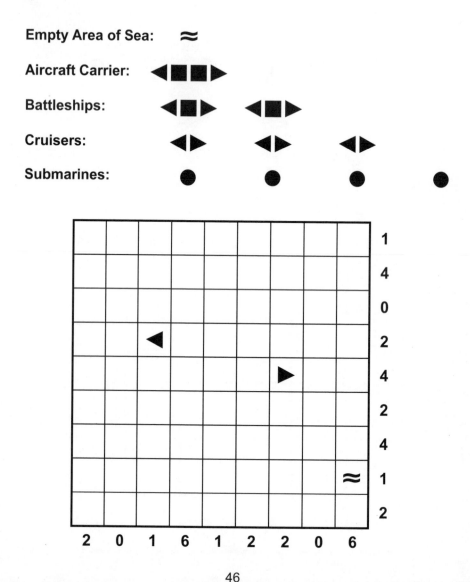

ELIMINATOR

Every oval shape contains a different letter of the alphabet from A to K inclusive. Use the clues to determine their locations. Reference in the clues to 'due' means in any location along the same horizontal or vertical line.

1 C is due west of G, which is next to and north of J.
2 J is due north of B, which is next to and east of D.
3 F is due north of H, which is both further north and further east than I.
4 K is due west of A, which is both further east and further south than E.

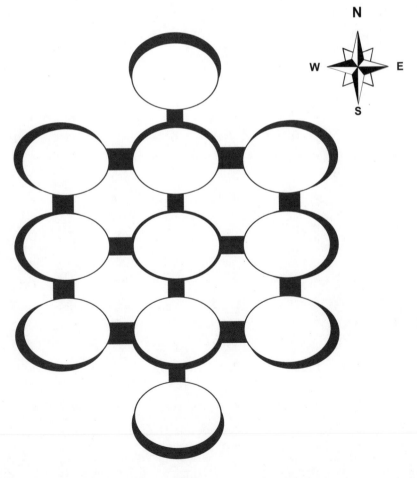

SLITHERLINK

43

Draw a single continuous loop, by connecting the dots. No line may cross the path of another.

The figure inside each set of any four surrounding dots indicates the total number of surrounding lines.

```
3       3   2   1   3               3

2           2   2   3   2   1       2

2   1       3   1               3   3

    1   1       0           0   2   1

    2           2   3           2       3

2       0           0   2           0

    2   3       2               2   0

2           0   2       1   0           1

2           2   1   1       1       3

        2       3           3       1   2

1   0           2   2       2   1   1

            3                       2

    1           3       1       1   2
```

PIECEWORK

Place all twelve of the pieces into the grid. Any may be rotated or flipped over, but none may touch another, not even diagonally.

The numbers outside the grid refer to the number of consecutive black squares; and each block is separated from the others by at least one white square. For instance, '3 2' could refer to a row with none, one or more white squares, then three black squares, then at least one white square, then two more black squares, followed by any number of white squares.

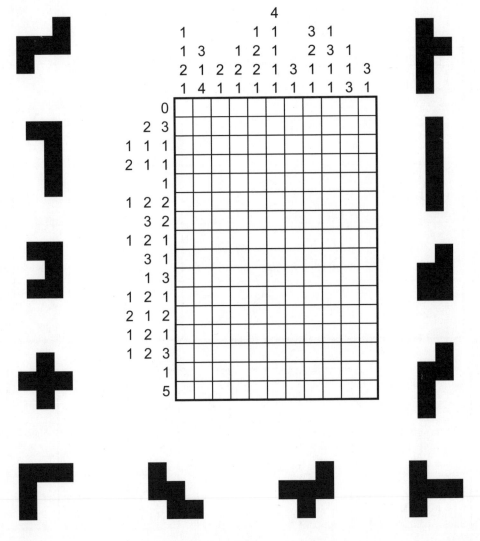

WHERE THE L?

Twelve L-shapes (three pieces of each of the four kinds shown below) need to be inserted in the grid and each L has one hole in it.

Any piece may be turned or flipped over before being put in the grid. No pieces of the same kind touch, even at a corner. The pieces fit together so well that you cannot see any spaces between them; only the holes show. Can you tell where the Ls are?

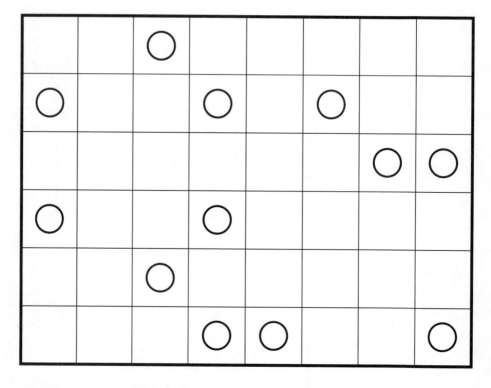

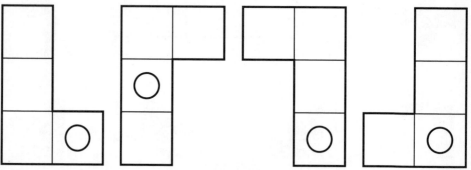

In this puzzle, an amateur coin collector has been out with his metal detector, searching for booty. He didn't have time to dig up all the coins he found, so has made a grid map, showing their locations, in the hope that if he loses the map, at least no-one else will understand it... However, he didn't count on YOU coming across the strange grid (as seen here). Will you be able to discover the correct number of coins and their precise locations?

Those squares containing numbers are empty, but where a number appears in a square, it indicates how many coins are located in the squares (up to a maximum of eight) surrounding the numbered one, touching it at any corner or side. There is only one coin in any individual square.

Place a circle into every square containing a coin.

			2	2		3	
1							
		2		2	3	2	2
1			1				
		1				1	
0			2		1	2	
		3				2	0
2							2
					4		
	3	2	4	4			
	1						2
		2		3	4		

BOX CLEVER

When the box below is folded to form a cube, just one of the five options (A, B, C, D or E) can be produced. Which?

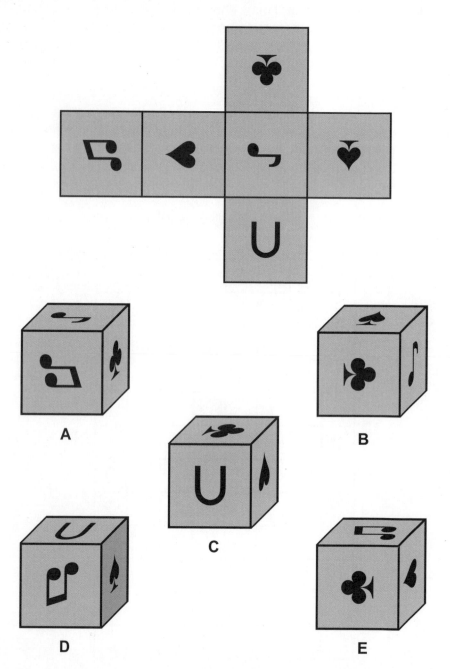

Each of these squares should contain one or more symbols from the numbered square to the left of its particular horizontal row, plus one or more symbols from the lettered square above its particular vertical column. However, one square doesn't follow this rule. Which is the odd one out?

	A	B	C	D	E	F
	◄ ¶	‡ ☼	♣ ¿	♦ #	♪ ≈	Σ $
1	E π	E☼ E¶	♣ π	π #	♪E π≈	πΣ $
2	♠ &	& ◄¶	‡& ♠	♣ ♣	♠ #	♠♪ &	&$ Σ
3	6 ►	►¶ ◄	‡6 ☼	♣► ¿	♦# ►	6 ≈	6$ ►
4	ß §	§ ►¶	ß ☼‡	¿§ ß	§♦ #	§≈	ß Σ §
5	▲ ♥	◄▲ ♥	♥‡ ▲	♣♥ ▲¿	# ♦▲	▲♪ ♥	♥ $
6	▼ ♫	¶▼ ♫	‡☼ ▼	▼ ♫¿	♫ #	♫≈ ♪	▼♫ $
7	Δ φ	φ◄	Δ ‡φ	Δ♣ ¿	φΔ #♦	≈♪ Δφ	Σ$ Δ

TILE TWISTER

Place the eight tiles into the puzzle grid so that all adjacent numbers on each tile match up. Tiles may be rotated through 360 degrees, but none may be flipped over.

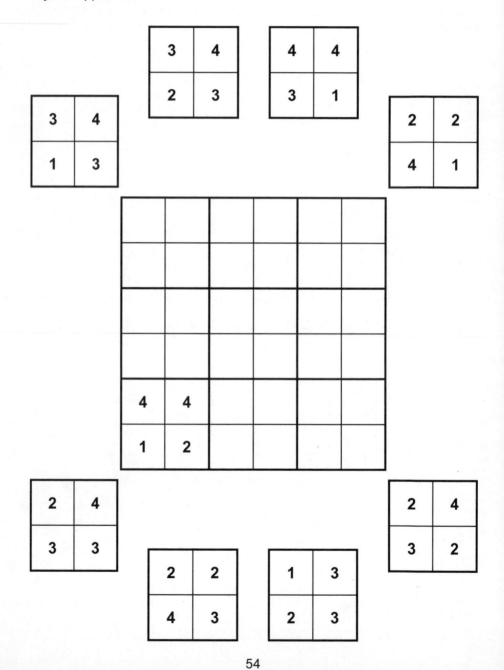

Every row and column of this grid should contain one each of the letters A, B, C, D, E and F. In addition, each of the six shapes (marked by thicker lines) should also contain one each of the letters A, B, C, D, E and F. Can you complete the grid?

A B C D E F

		B			A
			D	C	
		E			
	F				
B					

BATTLESHIPS

Can you place the vessels into the diagram? Some parts of vessels or sea squares have already been filled in. A number to the right or below a row or column refers to the number of occupied squares in that row or column.

Any vessel may be positioned horizontally or vertically, but no part of a vessel touches part of any other vessel, either horizontally, vertically or diagonally.

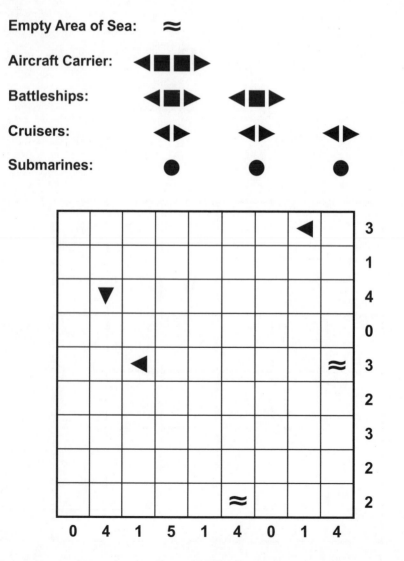

Every oval shape contains a different letter of the alphabet from A to K inclusive. Use the clues to determine their locations. Reference in the clues to 'due' means in any location along the same horizontal or vertical line.

1   E is due east of A, which is due south of F.

2   J is due south of G, which is due west of I.

3   D is due west of B, which is due north of K.

4   B is due west of C, which is due north of E.

5   K is both due north of H and due east of G.

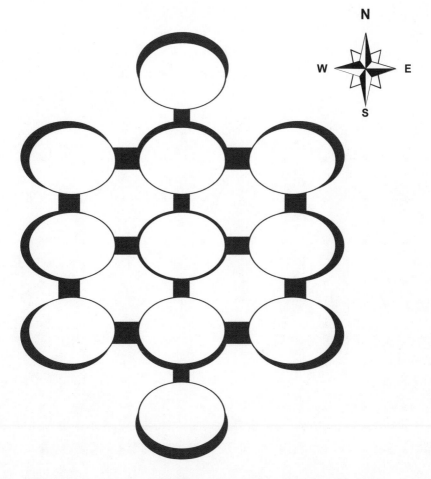

SLITHERLINK

Draw a single continuous loop, by connecting the dots. No line may cross the path of another.

The figure inside each set of any four surrounding dots indicates the total number of surrounding lines.

```
.  .  .  .  .  .  .  .  .  .  .  .
  3     1     2  2  1     3  3
.  .  .  .  .  .  .  .  .  .  .  .
  1           0  2        2
.  .  .  .  .  .  .  .  .  .  .  .
     0           0              1
.  .  .  .  .  .  .  .  .  .  .  .
  2  1        0     1  1     2
.  .  .  .  .  .  .  .  .  .  .  .
     1        1     2  3  1  2
.  .  .  .  .  .  .  .  .  .  .  .
1  1     1  1  3        2     3
.  .  .  .  .  .  .  .  .  .  .  .
  1     1  2              0
.  .  .  .  .  .  .  .  .  .  .  .
  1     1        1           2
.  .  .  .  .  .  .  .  .  .  .  .
     1        3  2  2     3  1
.  .  .  .  .  .  .  .  .  .  .  .
  3           1  1  2     1
.  .  .  .  .  .  .  .  .  .  .  .
  1     3     2     3
.  .  .  .  .  .  .  .  .  .  .  .
  1     2     1        1  1  3
.  .  .  .  .  .  .  .  .  .  .  .
     2        1        2     3
.  .  .  .  .  .  .  .  .  .  .  .
```

Place all twelve of the pieces into the grid. Any may be rotated or flipped over, but none may touch another, not even diagonally.

The numbers outside the grid refer to the number of consecutive black squares; and each block is separated from the others by at least one white square. For instance, '3 2' could refer to a row with none, one or more white squares, then three black squares, then at least one white square, then two more black squares, followed by any number of white squares.

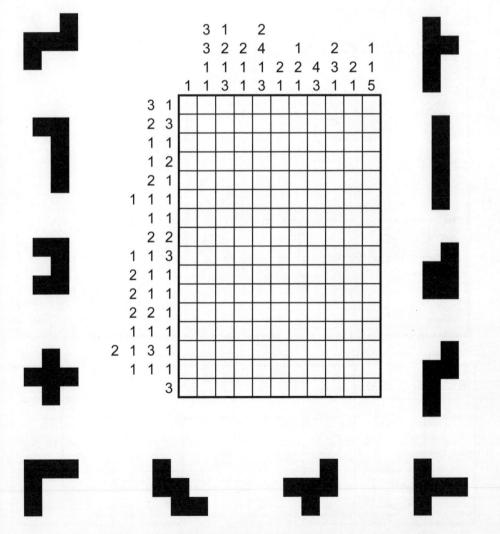

WHERE THE L?

Twelve L-shapes (three pieces of each of the four kinds shown below) need to be inserted in the grid and each L has one hole in it.

Any piece may be turned or flipped over before being put in the grid. No pieces of the same kind touch, even at a corner. The pieces fit together so well that you cannot see any spaces between them; only the holes show. Can you tell where the Ls are?

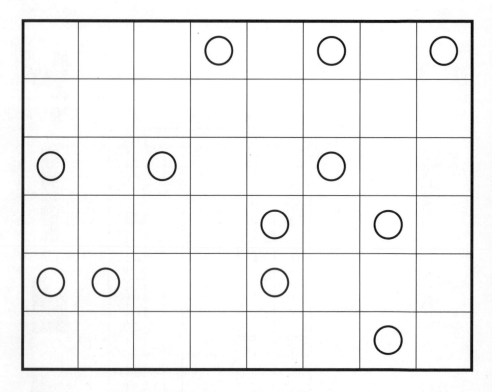

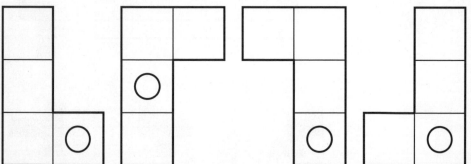

In this puzzle, an amateur coin collector has been out with his metal detector, searching for booty. He didn't have time to dig up all the coins he found, so has made a grid map, showing their locations, in the hope that if he loses the map, at least no-one else will understand it... However, he didn't count on YOU coming across the strange grid (as seen here). Will you be able to discover the correct number of coins and their precise locations?

Those squares containing numbers are empty, but where a number appears in a square, it indicates how many coins are located in the squares (up to a maximum of eight) surrounding the numbered one, touching it at any corner or side. There is only one coin in any individual square.

Place a circle into every square containing a coin.

					1		0
1	2	3		3			
		3				0	
1				2	0		
			3				
2		2				1	1
						3	
	2		5				
			3	2			3
	1						
		3			4		
1			2			2	

BOX CLEVER

When the box below is folded to form a cube, just one of the five options (A, B, C, D or E) can be produced. Which?

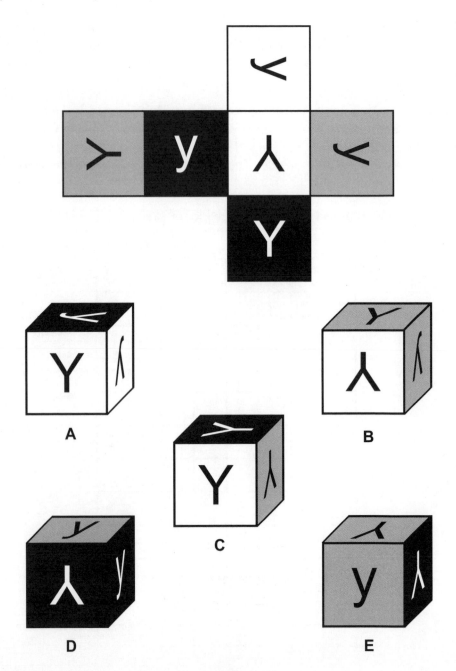

Each of these squares should contain one or more symbols from the numbered square to the left of its particular horizontal row, plus one or more symbols from the lettered square above its particular vertical column. However, one square doesn't follow this rule. Which is the odd one out?

	A	B	C	D	E	F
	Θ Π	€ $	‡ ©	◆ #	♪ μ	Σ ♂
1	∩ π	Θ Π π ∩	∩ π $ €	© ‡ π	◆ π ∩#	♪ π	♂ ∩ Σ
2	♠ Ψ	Ψ Π	Ψ ♠ € $	‡ © Ψ ♠	♠ Ψ ◆	♠ μ ♪ Ψ	Σ Ψ ♂
3	£ ▶	Θ ▶	£ ▶ $ €	£ ‡ ©	◆ £ #▶	μ ▶ £	▶ £ Σ
4	Ю §	Θ Π Ю §	§ Ю € $	§ © ‡ Ю	§ ◆ Ю	Ю ♪ §	Σ Ю §
5	Δ א	Π Θ א	$ € א	א ©	Δ א ◆	א μ Δ	Δ Σ א
6	▲ ٩	Π Θ ▲	€ ٩ ▲	© ▲ ٩	◆ ▲ ٩	μ ٩ ♪	٩ ♂ Σ
7	▼ Я	Π Я Θ ▼	Я € ▼ $	‡ Я ©	Я ▼ #	♪ ▼ Я	♂ ▼ Я

TILE TWISTER

Place the eight tiles into the puzzle grid so that all adjacent numbers on each tile match up. Tiles may be rotated through 360 degrees, but none may be flipped over.

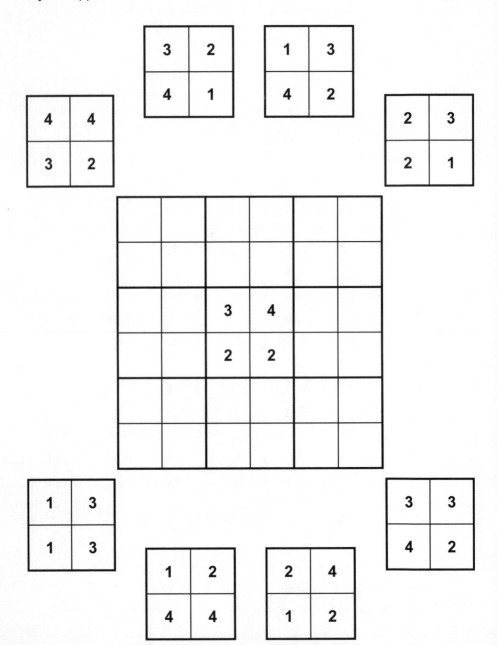

Every row and column of this grid should contain one each of the letters A, B, C, D, E and F. In addition, each of the six shapes (marked by thicker lines) should also contain one each of the letters A, B, C, D, E and F. Can you complete the grid?

A B C D E F

	A				
			C		B
	C				
					D
F			E		

BATTLESHIPS

Can you place the vessels into the diagram? Some parts of vessels or sea squares have already been filled in. A number to the right or below a row or column refers to the number of occupied squares in that row or column.

Any vessel may be positioned horizontally or vertically, but no part of a vessel touches part of any other vessel, either horizontally, vertically or diagonally.

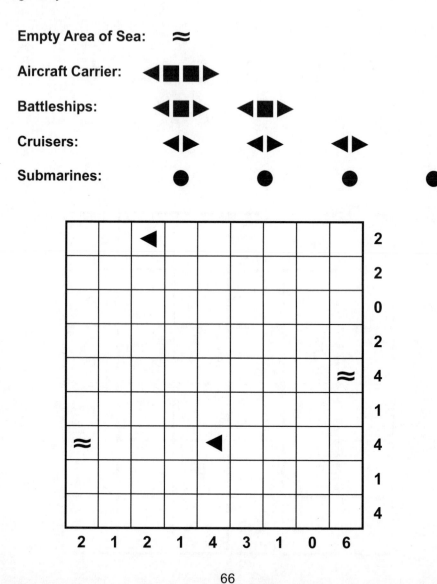

Every oval shape contains a different letter of the alphabet from A to K inclusive. Use the clues to determine their locations. Reference in the clues to 'due' means in any location along the same horizontal or vertical line.

1 A is both due north of B and due east of C.
2 D is both due east of F and due south of (but not next to) E.
3 K is due west of G, which is both due north of H and due west of I.
4 A is due east of J, which is next to and north of K.

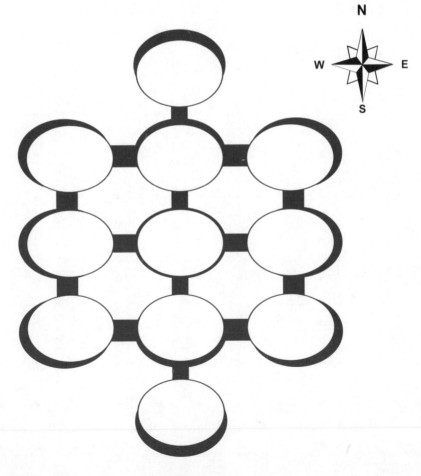

SLITHERLINK

Draw a single continuous loop, by connecting the dots. No line may cross the path of another.

The figure inside each set of any four surrounding dots indicates the total number of surrounding lines.

PIECEWORK

Place all twelve of the pieces into the grid. Any may be rotated or flipped over, but none may touch another, not even diagonally.

The numbers outside the grid refer to the number of consecutive black squares; and each block is separated from the others by at least one white square. For instance, '3 2' could refer to a row with none, one or more white squares, then three black squares, then at least one white square, then two more black squares, followed by any number of white squares.

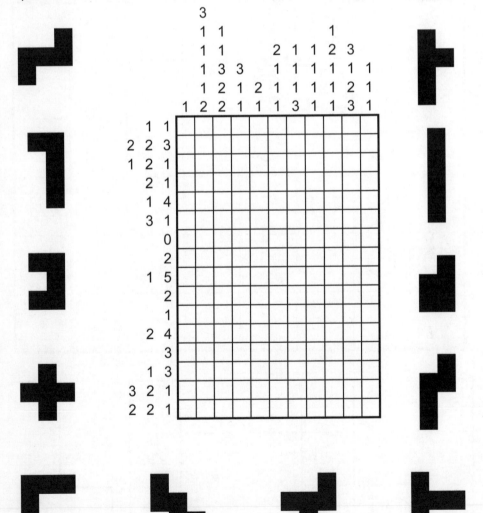

WHERE THE L?

Twelve L-shapes (three pieces of each of the four kinds shown below) need to be inserted in the grid and each L has one hole in it.

Any piece may be turned or flipped over before being put in the grid. No pieces of the same kind touch, even at a corner. The pieces fit together so well that you cannot see any spaces between them; only the holes show. Can you tell where the Ls are?

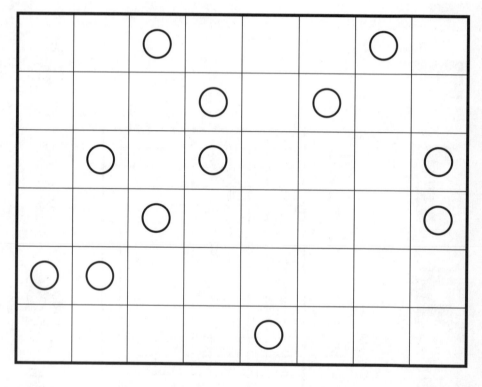

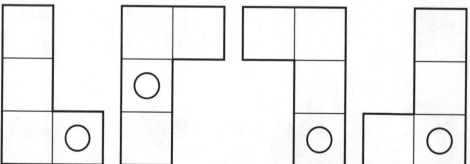

In this puzzle, an amateur coin collector has been out with his metal detector, searching for booty. He didn't have time to dig up all the coins he found, so has made a grid map, showing their locations, in the hope that if he loses the map, at least no-one else will understand it... However, he didn't count on YOU coming across the strange grid (as seen here). Will you be able to discover the correct number of coins and their precise locations?

Those squares containing numbers are empty, but where a number appears in a square, it indicates how many coins are located in the squares (up to a maximum of eight) surrounding the numbered one, touching it at any corner or side. There is only one coin in any individual square.

Place a circle into every square containing a coin.

1					2	1	1
		3				1	
		4		2			
4			2				
		1					1
2			1		1	2	
		2					
2				5		3	
		3				4	
1							1
	1		2				2
0			0		2		

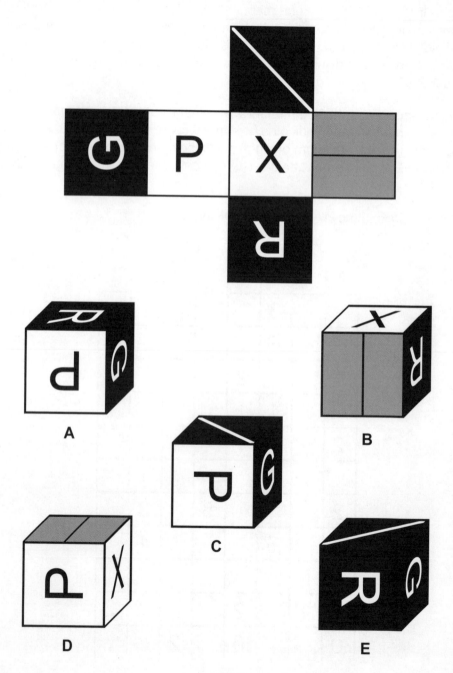

BOX CLEVER

When the box below is folded to form a cube, just one of the five options (A, B, C, D or E) can be produced. Which?

A

B

C

D

E

SYMBOLISM

Each of these squares should contain one or more symbols from the numbered square to the left of its particular horizontal row, plus one or more symbols from the lettered square above its particular vertical column. However, one square doesn't follow this rule. Which is the odd one out?

	A	B	C	D	E	F
	♦ #	Σ ☼	♪ ¶	◀ ≈	‡ ¿	♣ $
1 △ ♥	♦△ ♥#	☼Σ ♥	♥¶ ♪	◀ ♥	‡ △¿	△ ♣♥
2 ▼ φ	♦# φ	▼ ☼	¶▼ φ♪	▼ ◀≈	¿ φ▼	φ▼ $
3 ▲ ♫	# ♦	☼ Σ♫	♪▲ ¶	≈ ♫◀	‡♫ ¿	▲$ ♫
4 Ω §	#§ Ω	ΩΣ §	§ ¶	Ω≈ §	§ ¿Ω	Ω♣ $
5 £ ▶	♦▶ £	£Σ ☼	♪ £	▶◀	£‡ ¿	▶$ ♣
6 ♠ ß	# ♠	ß♠ Σ	¶ ß	◀ß ≈	♠ ¿‡	$♣ ♠
7 ∩ π	♦π ∩	π☼	∩¶	π≈ ◀∩	π ‡	♣$ ∩

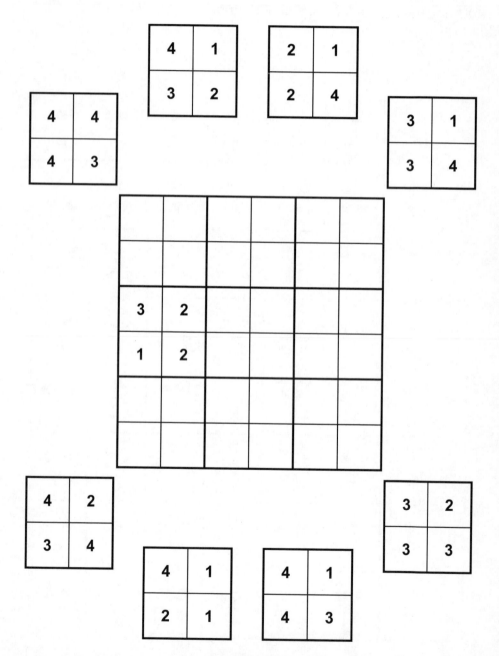

TILE TWISTER

Place the eight tiles into the puzzle grid so that all adjacent numbers on each tile match up. Tiles may be rotated through 360 degrees, but none may be flipped over.

Every row and column of this grid should contain one each of the letters A, B, C, D, E and F. In addition, each of the six shapes (marked by thicker lines) should also contain one each of the letters A, B, C, D, E and F. Can you complete the grid?

A B C D E F

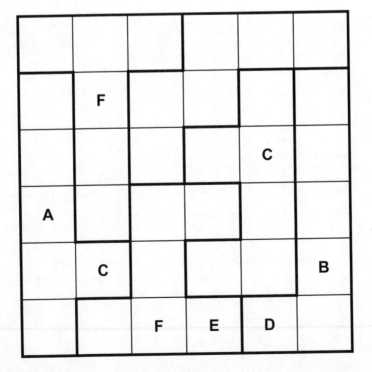

BATTLESHIPS

Can you place the vessels into the diagram? Some parts of vessels or sea squares have already been filled in. A number to the right or below a row or column refers to the number of occupied squares in that row or column.

Any vessel may be positioned horizontally or vertically, but no part of a vessel touches part of any other vessel, either horizontally, vertically or diagonally.

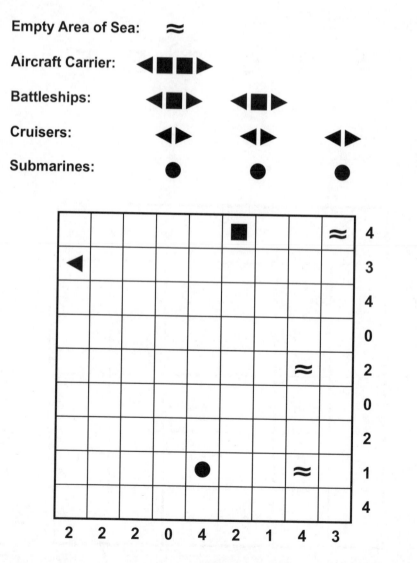

ELIMINATOR

ELIMINATOR

Every oval shape contains a different letter of the alphabet from A to K inclusive. Use the clues to determine their locations. Reference in the clues to 'due' means in any location along the same horizontal or vertical line.

1 F is due north of D, which is due west of E.

2 D is due north of J, which is due west of H.

3 B is due west of I, which is due north of K.

4 A is due south of B.

5 C is due north of H, which is due west of G.

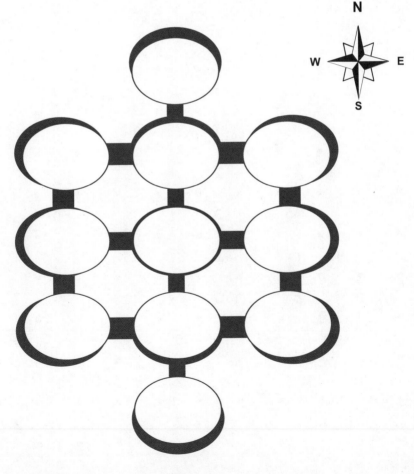

SLITHERLINK

Draw a single continuous loop, by connecting the dots. No line may cross the path of another.

The figure inside each set of any four surrounding dots indicates the total number of surrounding lines.

```
.   .   .   .   .   .   .   .   .   .   .   .
        1           3   2   2       1
.   .   .   .   .   .   .   .   .   .   .   .
  3   3       3   2       2       2
.   .   .   .   .   .   .   .   .   .   .   .
  1   2       2       1   2   1   3
.   .   .   .   .   .   .   .   .   .   .   .
            1           2       0           1
.   .   .   .   .   .   .   .   .   .   .   .
          2   1   1               1
.   .   .   .   .   .   .   .   .   .   .   .
                1       0       3       3
.   .   .   .   .   .   .   .   .   .   .   .
  1   1   2       2
.   .   .   .   .   .   .   .   .   .   .   .
                3               0   3   1
.   .   .   .   .   .   .   .   .   .   .   .
  2   0   1   2   2                       1
.   .   .   .   .   .   .   .   .   .   .   .
          2       3
.   .   .   .   .   .   .   .   .   .   .   .
            3       0               0
.   .   .   .   .   .   .   .   .   .   .   .
  1       0   3       2       1
.   .   .   .   .   .   .   .   .   .   .   .
                    2   1           2   0
.   .   .   .   .   .   .   .   .   .   .   .
```

PIECEWORK

Place all twelve of the pieces into the grid. Any may be rotated or flipped over, but none may touch another, not even diagonally.

The numbers outside the grid refer to the number of consecutive black squares; and each block is separated from the others by at least one white square. For instance, '3 2' could refer to a row with none, one or more white squares, then three black squares, then at least one white square, then two more black squares, followed by any number of white squares.

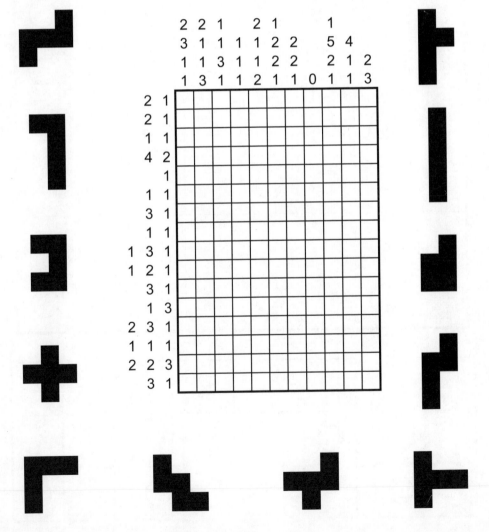

WHERE THE L?

Twelve L-shapes (three pieces of each of the four kinds shown below) need to be inserted in the grid and each L has one hole in it.

Any piece may be turned or flipped over before being put in the grid. No pieces of the same kind touch, even at a corner. The pieces fit together so well that you cannot see any spaces between them; only the holes show. Can you tell where the Ls are?

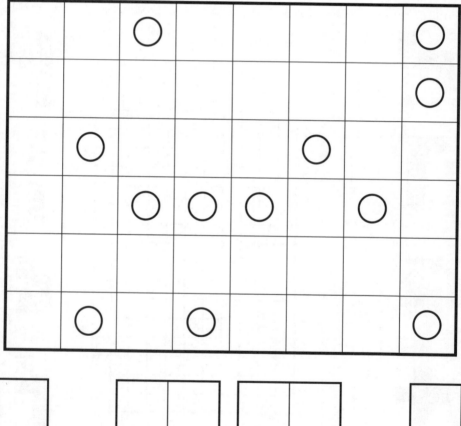

In this puzzle, an amateur coin collector has been out with his metal detector, searching for booty. He didn't have time to dig up all the coins he found, so has made a grid map, showing their locations, in the hope that if he loses the map, at least no-one else will understand it... However, he didn't count on YOU coming across the strange grid (as seen here). Will you be able to discover the correct number of coins and their precise locations?

Those squares containing numbers are empty, but where a number appears in a square, it indicates how many coins are located in the squares (up to a maximum of eight) surrounding the numbered one, touching it at any corner or side. There is only one coin in any individual square.

Place a circle into every square containing a coin.

1			0	0			0
			1				
	3					1	
1				2			
0		4		3		2	
						3	2
0			4		3		
2							
			5	3	3	2	
	3			2			1
	2		4	4			
				3			1

BOX CLEVER

When the box below is folded to form a cube, just one of the five options (A, B, C, D or E) can be produced. Which?

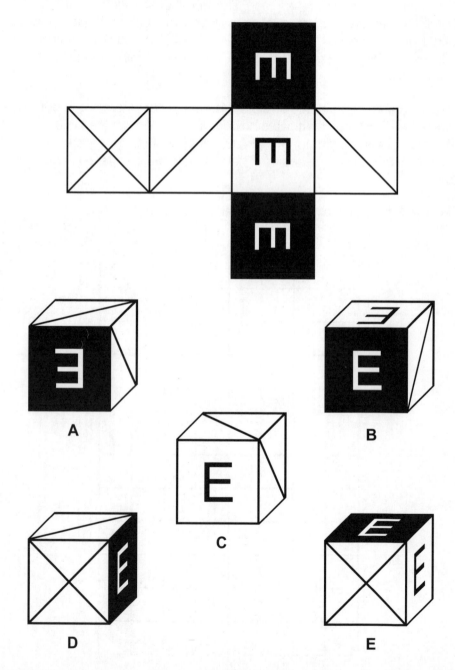

Each of these squares should contain one or more symbols from the numbered square to the left of its particular horizontal row, plus one or more symbols from the lettered square above its particular vertical column. However, one square doesn't follow this rule. Which is the odd one out?

	A	B	C	D	E	F
	◄ ≈	♣ $	‡ ¿	# ♦	♪ ¶	☼ Σ
1 §Ω	◄§ Ω	§Ω ♣$	‡¿ Ω	Ω# ♦§	¶♪ Ω§	ΣΩ ☼
2 ♠ß	♠◄ ß≈	$ß	ß‡ ¿♠	#ß ♦	¶ ♠♪	☼Σ ß♠
3 £►	≈£ ►◄	► ♣£	£► ‡	♦ £#	♪► ¶	£ Σ☼
4 π∩	≈ ◄∩	π$ ♣	π∩ ‡	∩♦ #	∩π ¶♪	∩Σ ☼π
5 ♥Δ	Δ◄ ♥	$♣ ♥Δ	¿ Δ‡	#♥ ♦Δ	Δ♥ ♪¶	☼Δ Σ
6 ▲♫	◄♫ ≈	$♣ ♫▲	▲♫ ¿	♫ ▲	¶▲	♫ ▲Σ
7 φ▼	φ≈ ▼	▼φ ♣$	‡¿ ▼	φ♦ ▼#	▼♪	Σ▼ ☼

TILE TWISTER

Place the eight tiles into the puzzle grid so that all adjacent numbers on each tile match up. Tiles may be rotated through 360 degrees, but none may be flipped over.

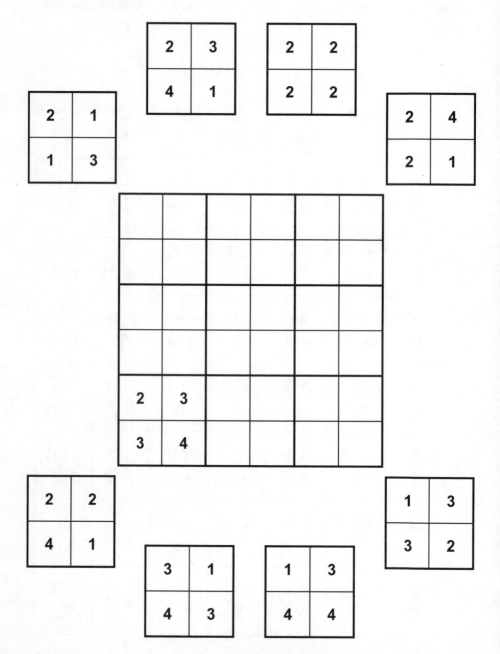

LOGI-6

Every row and column of this grid should contain one each of the letters A, B, C, D, E and F. In addition, each of the six shapes (marked by thicker lines) should also contain one each of the letters A, B, C, D, E and F. Can you complete the grid?

A B C D E F

BATTLESHIPS

Can you place the vessels into the diagram? Some parts of vessels or sea squares have already been filled in. A number to the right or below a row or column refers to the number of occupied squares in that row or column.

Any vessel may be positioned horizontally or vertically, but no part of a vessel touches part of any other vessel, either horizontally, vertically or diagonally.

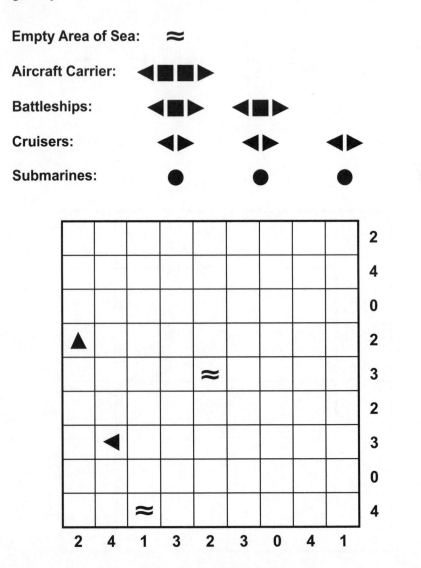

Every oval shape contains a different letter of the alphabet from A to K inclusive. Use the clues to determine their locations. Reference in the clues to 'due' means in any location along the same horizontal or vertical line.

1   G is due north of K, which is next to and west of J.

2   H is next to and east of F, which is next to and north of B.

3   D is due east of A, which is next to and north of E.

4   C is further north than J, but further south than G.

5   I is due south of B, which is further north than K.

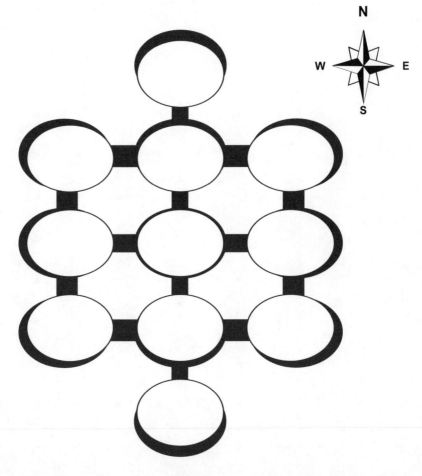

SLITHERLINK

Draw a single continuous loop, by connecting the dots. No line may cross the path of another.

The figure inside each set of any four surrounding dots indicates the total number of surrounding lines.

```
·   ·   ·   ·   ·   ·   ·   ·   ·   ·   ·   ·
      1   2           3
·   ·   ·   ·   ·   ·   ·   ·   ·   ·   ·   ·
  2                       2       1   1   2
·   ·   ·   ·   ·   ·   ·   ·   ·   ·   ·   ·
  3   3       1   3           2   0       1
·   ·   ·   ·   ·   ·   ·   ·   ·   ·   ·   ·
  2       0       2       2   0
·   ·   ·   ·   ·   ·   ·   ·   ·   ·   ·   ·
      0               1       0   1   2
·   ·   ·   ·   ·   ·   ·   ·   ·   ·   ·   ·
  1       1   1           0   2   2
·   ·   ·   ·   ·   ·   ·   ·   ·   ·   ·   ·
  3   1   1   1   2   2
·   ·   ·   ·   ·   ·   ·   ·   ·   ·   ·   ·
              2                           2
·   ·   ·   ·   ·   ·   ·   ·   ·   ·   ·   ·
      0   2           1   2   1       2
·   ·   ·   ·   ·   ·   ·   ·   ·   ·   ·   ·
      1               2   1       2
·   ·   ·   ·   ·   ·   ·   ·   ·   ·   ·   ·
  3               1   2           3
·   ·   ·   ·   ·   ·   ·   ·   ·   ·   ·   ·
      1           1   2   2   2   2   2
·   ·   ·   ·   ·   ·   ·   ·   ·   ·   ·   ·
  2   2       3       3   1   2       2   2
·   ·   ·   ·   ·   ·   ·   ·   ·   ·   ·   ·
```

Place all twelve of the pieces into the grid. Any may be rotated or flipped over, but none may touch another, not even diagonally.

The numbers outside the grid refer to the number of consecutive black squares; and each block is separated from the others by at least one white square. For instance, '3 2' could refer to a row with none, one or more white squares, then three black squares, then at least one white square, then two more black squares, followed by any number of white squares.

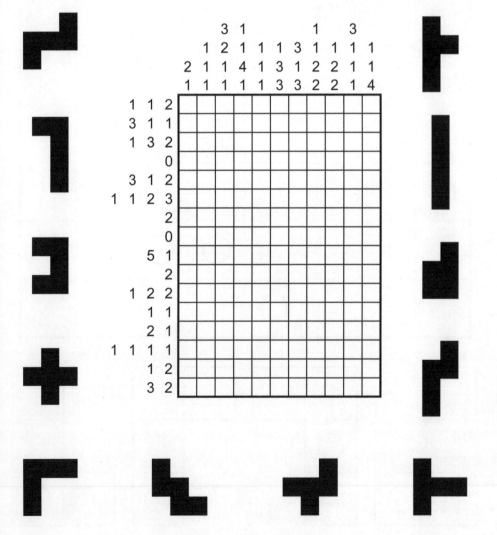

WHERE THE L?

Twelve L-shapes (three pieces of each of the four kinds shown below) need to be inserted in the grid and each L has one hole in it.

Any piece may be turned or flipped over before being put in the grid. No pieces of the same kind touch, even at a corner. The pieces fit together so well that you cannot see any spaces between them; only the holes show. Can you tell where the Ls are?

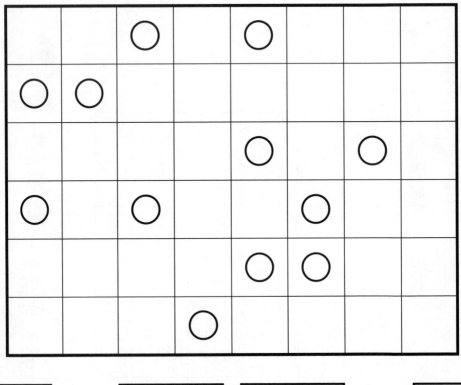

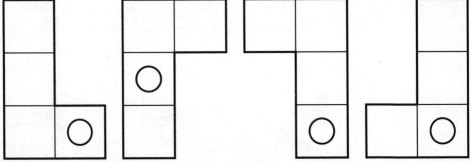

COIN COLLECTING

In this puzzle, an amateur coin collector has been out with his metal detector, searching for booty. He didn't have time to dig up all the coins he found, so has made a grid map, showing their locations, in the hope that if he loses the map, at least no-one else will understand it... However, he didn't count on YOU coming across the strange grid (as seen here). Will you be able to discover the correct number of coins and their precise locations?

Those squares containing numbers are empty, but where a number appears in a square, it indicates how many coins are located in the squares (up to a maximum of eight) surrounding the numbered one, touching it at any corner or side. There is only one coin in any individual square.

Place a circle into every square containing a coin.

0						3	
			4				
0					3		0
			3				
		2			3		
	2		4		2		1
	3	4		1			
				1		1	
2	4				1	1	
	3			2	1		
		3					
2				2		1	

BOX CLEVER

When the box below is folded to form a cube, just one of the five options (A, B, C, D or E) can be produced. Which?

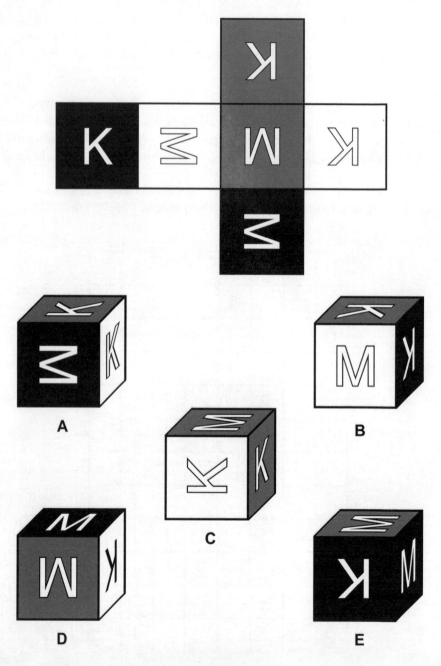

A

B

C

D

E

Each of these squares should contain one or more symbols from the numbered square to the left of its particular horizontal row, plus one or more symbols from the lettered square above its particular vertical column. However, one square doesn't follow this rule. Which is the odd one out?

	A	B	C	D	E	F
	◄ Ю	T Ж	ψ ¿	♫ ▲	♪ ☼	Σ Θ
1 ⇧ ★	Ю★ ◄	ЖT ⇧★	⇧ψ ¿	▲♫ ★⇧	♪★ ☼⇧	Θ⇧ Σ
2 F Ħ	ĦF ◄Ю	TЖ Ħ	ψF ¿	Ħ♫ F▲	F♪ Ħ☼	Θ FĦ
3 ¥ ☺	☺¥ ◄	☺T Ж	☺¥ ¿	¥☺ ▲♫	¥♪ ☺	☺ ΘΣ
4 ∩ ¶	∩ Ю	Ж ¶∩	∩¶ ψ	▲∩ ¶	☼¶ ∩	Θ¶
5 Ø 7	7◄ Øю	TØ Ж7	¿ ψ7	♫▲ 7Ø	♪☼ Ø7	ΣØ Θ
6 ♣ §	◄§ Ю♣	§♣ Ж	♣§ ¿ψ	♫§	§ ♣☼	Σ§ ♣Ø
7 ♥ ω	◄ω ♥	♥Ж ωT	ω♥ ψ¿	ω▲ ♫	☼♪ ω♥	♥ω Σ

93

TILE TWISTER

Place the eight tiles into the puzzle grid so that all adjacent numbers on each tile match up. Tiles may be rotated through 360 degrees, but none may be flipped over.

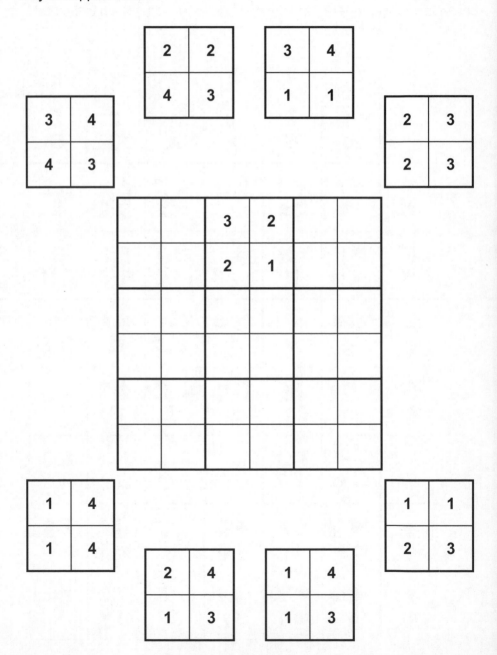

Every row and column of this grid should contain one each of the letters A, B, C, D, E and F. In addition, each of the six shapes (marked by thicker lines) should also contain one each of the letters A, B, C, D, E and F. Can you complete the grid?

A B C D E F

		C			
				B	A
	D			C	
E					
F					

BATTLESHIPS

Can you place the vessels into the diagram? Some parts of vessels or sea squares have already been filled in. A number to the right or below a row or column refers to the number of occupied squares in that row or column.

Any vessel may be positioned horizontally or vertically, but no part of a vessel touches part of any other vessel, either horizontally, vertically or diagonally.

Empty Area of Sea: ≈

Aircraft Carrier: ◀■■▶

Battleships: ◀■▶ ◀■▶

Cruisers: ◀▶ ◀▶ ◀▶

Submarines: ● ● ● ●

Grid column totals: 1 3 3 0 6 1 0 6 0

Grid row totals (top to bottom): 3 2 2 3 2 1 3 2 2

Every oval shape contains a different letter of the alphabet from A to K inclusive. Use the clues to determine their locations. Reference in the clues to 'due' means in any location along the same horizontal or vertical line.

1 A is both due south of D and due west of E.
2 J is due west of F, which is both due north of I and due west of B.
3 D is both due west of C and due south of G.
4 K is both due north of H and due south of J.

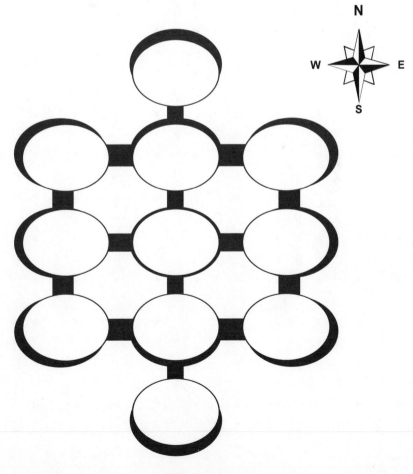

SLITHERLINK

Draw a single continuous loop, by connecting the dots. No line may cross the path of another.

The figure inside each set of any four surrounding dots indicates the total number of surrounding lines.

PIECEWORK

Place all twelve of the pieces into the grid. Any may be rotated or flipped over, but none may touch another, not even diagonally.

The numbers outside the grid refer to the number of consecutive black squares; and each block is separated from the others by at least one white square. For instance, '3 2' could refer to a row with none, one or more white squares, then three black squares, then at least one white square, then two more black squares, followed by any number of white squares.

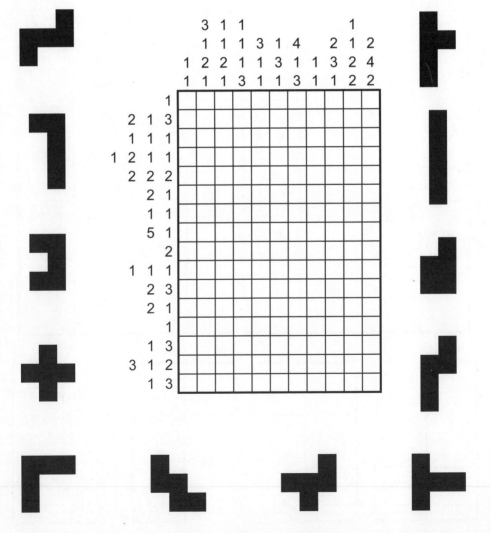

WHERE THE L?

Twelve L-shapes (three pieces of each of the four kinds shown below) need to be inserted in the grid and each L has one hole in it.

Any piece may be turned or flipped over before being put in the grid. No pieces of the same kind touch, even at a corner. The pieces fit together so well that you cannot see any spaces between them; only the holes show. Can you tell where the Ls are?

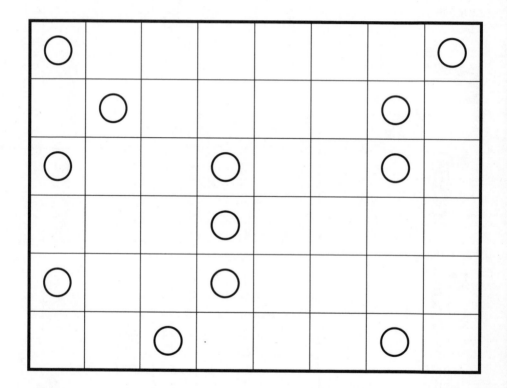

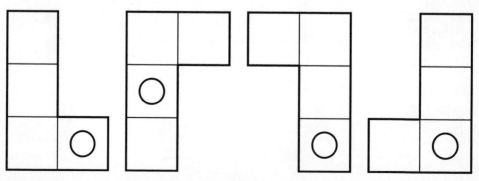

In this puzzle, an amateur coin collector has been out with his metal detector, searching for booty. He didn't have time to dig up all the coins he found, so has made a grid map, showing their locations, in the hope that if he loses the map, at least no-one else will understand it... However, he didn't count on YOU coming across the strange grid (as seen here). Will you be able to discover the correct number of coins and their precise locations?

Those squares containing numbers are empty, but where a number appears in a square, it indicates how many coins are located in the squares (up to a maximum of eight) surrounding the numbered one, touching it at any corner or side. There is only one coin in any individual square.

Place a circle into every square containing a coin.

		3				
1			4	3	2	
		4	3			
2	3			2		
		2	2		2	
	3	1			1	
2				2		
2	3	2				
	2	2				
4	3				2	
	3		1			
3		0		0		

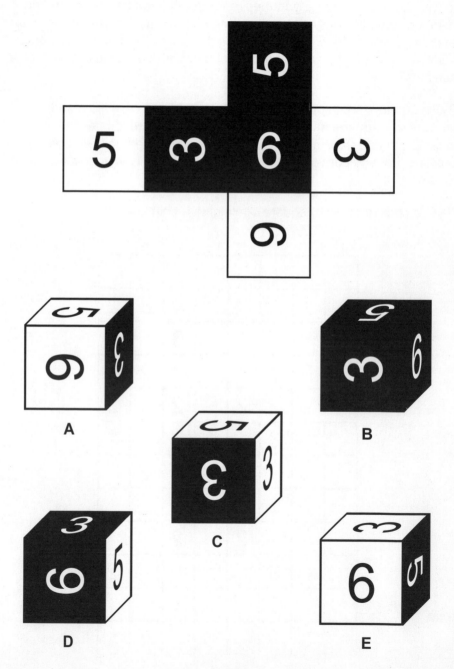

BOX CLEVER

When the box below is folded to form a cube, just one of the five options (A, B, C, D or E) can be produced. Which?

SYMBOLISM

Each of these squares should contain one or more symbols from the numbered square to the left of its particular horizontal row, plus one or more symbols from the lettered square above its particular vertical column. However, one square doesn't follow this rule. Which is the odd one out?

	A	B	C	D	E	F
	Σ 2	A $	‡ L	◄ R	F ¶	♦ 5
1 (3 §)	Σ3 §2	$A §	§ ‡L	§◄ R	3 ¶F	3 5
2 (♠ C)	♠ C	♠2 C	$ ♠	♠‡ L	C R♠	5 C
3 (Δ M)	Δ M	Δ Σ 2	M Δ	‡ Δ	◄Δ R	♦ Δ5
4 (▼ P)	▼ P	2Σ ▼	P A$	▼P L	R▼	F ¶P	▼5 P♦
5 (K ►)	K ►	►Σ 2	A ►K	KL ‡	R◄ ►	K ►F	► ♦K
6 (▲ 6)	▲ 6	Σ▲ 2	A $6	6 ▲L	6 ◄▲	¶ F6	▲ 5♦
7 (∩ 0)	∩ 0	Σ 2∩	∩$ 0A	‡ ∩0	R 0◄	∩ F¶	♦5 0

103

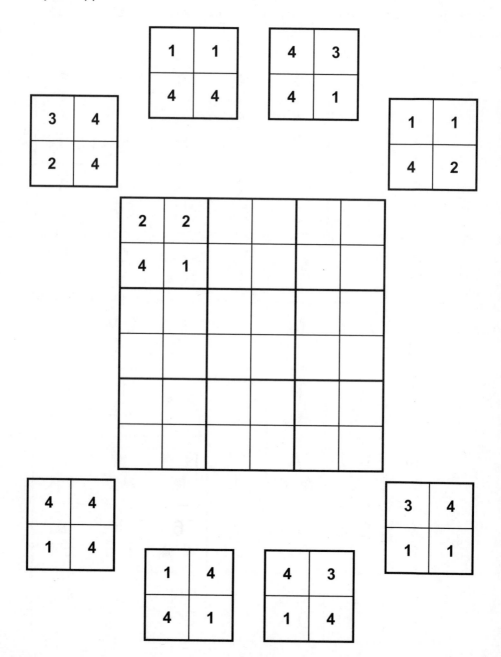

TILE TWISTER

Place the eight tiles into the puzzle grid so that all adjacent numbers on each tile match up. Tiles may be rotated through 360 degrees, but none may be flipped over.

Every row and column of this grid should contain one each of the letters A, B, C, D, E and F. In addition, each of the six shapes (marked by thicker lines) should also contain one each of the letters A, B, C, D, E and F. Can you complete the grid?

A B C D E F

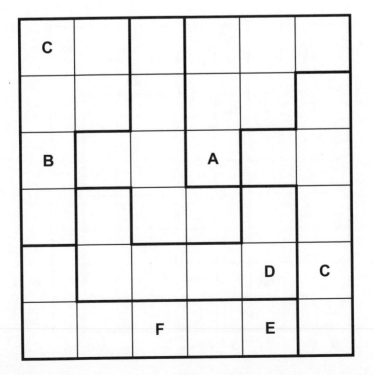

BATTLESHIPS

Can you place the vessels into the diagram? Some parts of vessels or sea squares have already been filled in. A number to the right or below a row or column refers to the number of occupied squares in that row or column.

Any vessel may be positioned horizontally or vertically, but no part of a vessel touches part of any other vessel, either horizontally, vertically or diagonally.

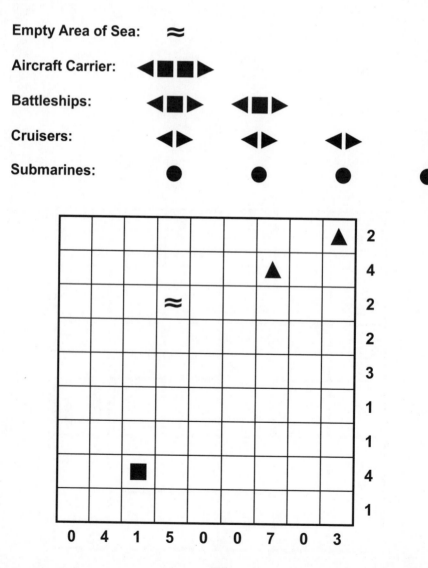

Every oval shape contains a different letter of the alphabet from A to K inclusive. Use the clues to determine their locations. Reference in the clues to 'due' means in any location along the same horizontal or vertical line.

1 A is next to and east of B, which is next to and north of C.

2 J is next to and west of D, which is due south of G.

3 I is next to and south of E, which is next to and east of H.

4 H is due north of D, which is further south than C.

5 F is further north than K, which is further west than F.

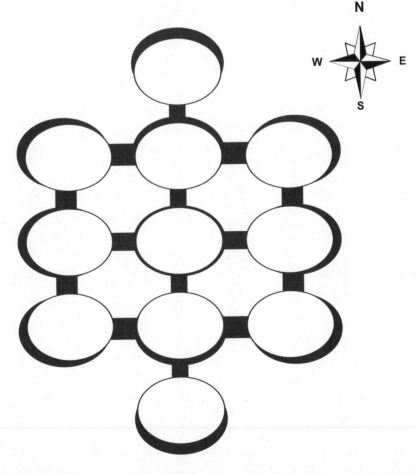

x

Place all twelve of the pieces into the grid. Any may be rotated or flipped over, but none may touch another, not even diagonally.

The numbers outside the grid refer to the number of consecutive black squares; and each block is separated from the others by at least one white square. For instance, '3 2' could refer to a row with none, one or more white squares, then three black squares, then at least one white square, then two more black squares, followed by any number of white squares.

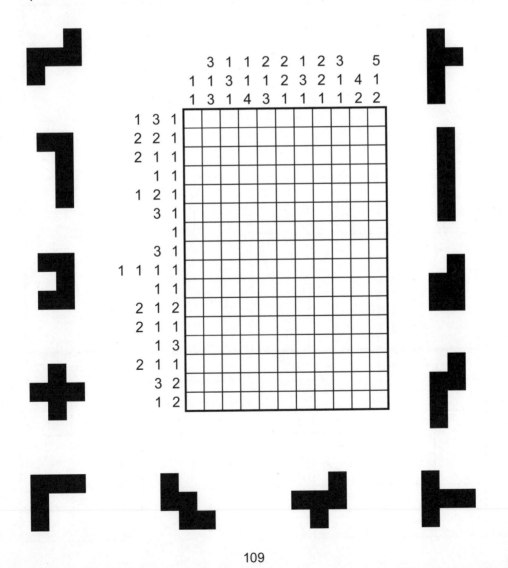

WHERE THE L?

Twelve L-shapes (three pieces of each of the four kinds shown below) need to be inserted in the grid and each L has one hole in it.

Any piece may be turned or flipped over before being put in the grid. No pieces of the same kind touch, even at a corner. The pieces fit together so well that you cannot see any spaces between them; only the holes show. Can you tell where the Ls are?

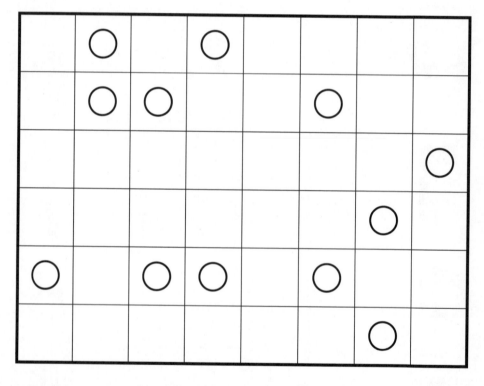

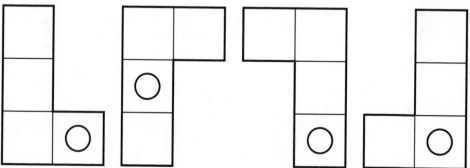

In this puzzle, an amateur coin collector has been out with his metal detector, searching for booty. He didn't have time to dig up all the coins he found, so has made a grid map, showing their locations, in the hope that if he loses the map, at least no-one else will understand it... However, he didn't count on YOU coming across the strange grid (as seen here). Will you be able to discover the correct number of coins and their precise locations?

Those squares containing numbers are empty, but where a number appears in a square, it indicates how many coins are located in the squares (up to a maximum of eight) surrounding the numbered one, touching it at any corner or side. There is only one coin in any individual square.

Place a circle into every square containing a coin.

1		0	1			1	
				1			
					0	1	
	2	1				2	
							1
1			5	3			
	2				1		2
				5		2	
0					1		
	1			4		4	
	0		3	4			
							3

BOX CLEVER

When the box below is folded to form a cube, just one of the five options (A, B, C, D or E) can be produced. Which?

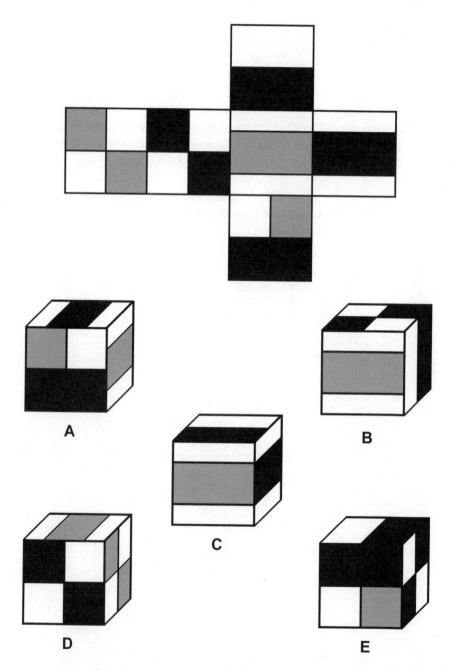

A

B

C

D

E

Each of these squares should contain one or more symbols from the numbered square to the left of its particular horizontal row, plus one or more symbols from the lettered square above its particular vertical column. However, one square doesn't follow this rule. Which is the odd one out?

	A	B	C	D	E	F
	◊ Ж	♥ ☼	ю §	♦ $	♪ %	Њ Д
1 θ ♪	Ж◊ θ	☼θ ♪	§θ ♪	♪ $♦	♪θ %♪	♪ Њ
2 Э ß	ß Ж Э◊	ß Э ☼	ю Э §	$♦ ß	% ß Э	Д ß Њ
3 ¥ ▼	◊Ж ¥▼	♥▼ ¥	¥ ю	▼ $♦	▼¥ %♪	¥Њ ▼
4 Ω ◄	◄Ω Ж◊	♥☼ Ω	Ω◄ ю§	♦◄ $	Ω ◄	Д ◄Ω
5 ю ⇑	◊⇑ юЖ	☼♥ ю⇑	§ ⇑ю	⇑ю $	ю% ⇑	ю Њ
6 ♀ =	Ж= ♀◊	=☼ ♥	ю♀ =	♦ =♀	%♪ =	=♀ Д
7 ▲ φ	◊φ ▲Ж	☼▲ φ♥	φ▲ §ю	$φ ♦	♪ ▲φ	▲ Њ

TILE TWISTER

Place the eight tiles into the puzzle grid so that all adjacent numbers on each tile match up. Tiles may be rotated through 360 degrees, but none may be flipped over.

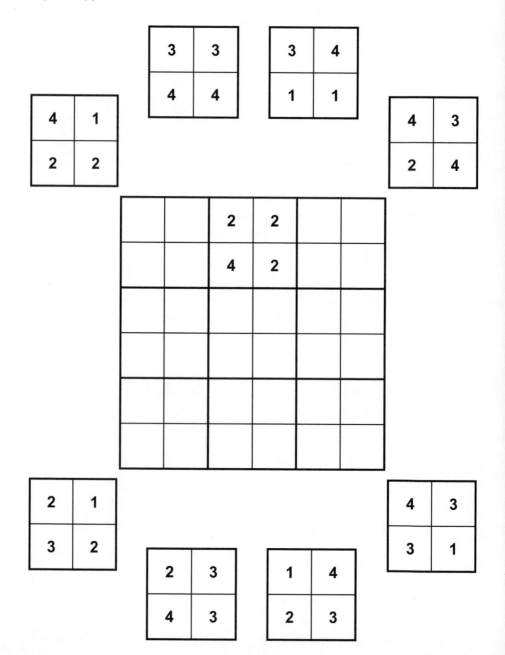

Every row and column of this grid should contain one each of the letters A, B, C, D, E and F. In addition, each of the six shapes (marked by thicker lines) should also contain one each of the letters A, B, C, D, E and F. Can you complete the grid?

A B C D E F

		B		A	
		C			
		F	E		D
E					

BATTLESHIPS

Can you place the vessels into the diagram? Some parts of vessels or sea squares have already been filled in. A number to the right or below a row or column refers to the number of occupied squares in that row or column.

Any vessel may be positioned horizontally or vertically, but no part of a vessel touches part of any other vessel, either horizontally, vertically or diagonally.

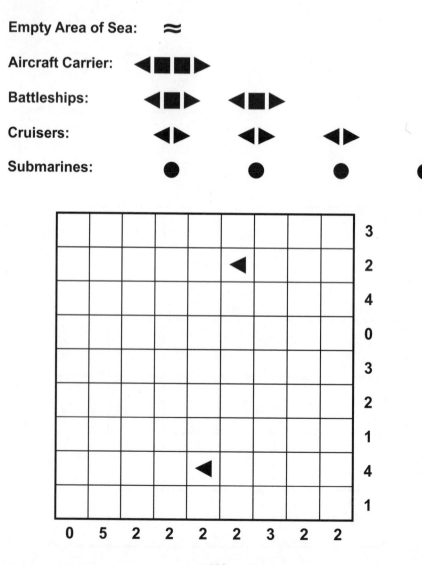

Every oval shape contains a different letter of the alphabet from A to K inclusive. Use the clues to determine their locations. Reference in the clues to 'due' means in any location along the same horizontal or vertical line.

1 A is both due west of I and due north of F, which is next to and south of H.
2 D is next to and north of J, which is due west of E.
3 E is both further east and further south than C, which is next to and south of B.
4 H is further south than K, which is due east of G.

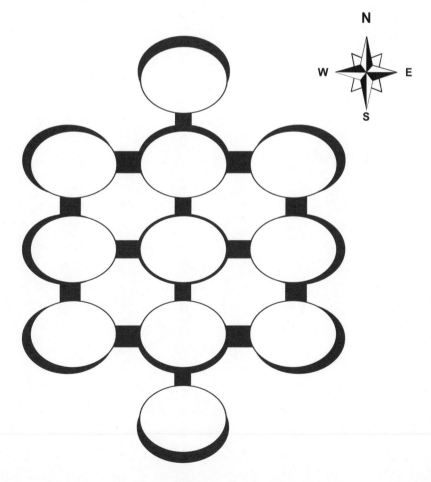

SLITHERLINK

Draw a single continuous loop, by connecting the dots. No line may cross the path of another.

The figure inside each set of any four surrounding dots indicates the total number of surrounding lines.

```
.   .   .   .   .   .   .   .   .   .   .   .
      1       2       3       2   1
.   .   .   .   .   .   .   .   .   .   .   .
  1   0                   2   1
.   .   .   .   .   .   .   .   .   .   .   .
      3   2   2   3   2           1   1   2
.   .   .   .   .   .   .   .   .   .   .   .
  2           0       1           1   3
.   .   .   .   .   .   .   .   .   .   .   .
                                      1
.   .   .   .   .   .   .   .   .   .   .   .
  0   3               0   2   2               1
.   .   .   .   .   .   .   .   .   .   .   .
  2       0           0   2           1   2
.   .   .   .   .   .   .   .   .   .   .   .
              0           3           1   1
.   .   .   .   .   .   .   .   .   .   .   .
  2   2       2       0   1       1
.   .   .   .   .   .   .   .   .   .   .   .
          3   2   2   0       3   2
.   .   .   .   .   .   .   .   .   .   .   .
  1           2       2   1               2
.   .   .   .   .   .   .   .   .   .   .   .
  2                           1   2
.   .   .   .   .   .   .   .   .   .   .   .
  2   2   1       0   2   2           3
.   .   .   .   .   .   .   .   .   .   .   .
```

PIECEWORK

Place all twelve of the pieces into the grid. Any may be rotated or flipped over, but none may touch another, not even diagonally.

The numbers outside the grid refer to the number of consecutive black squares; and each block is separated from the others by at least one white square. For instance, '3 2' could refer to a row with none, one or more white squares, then three black squares, then at least one white square, then two more black squares, followed by any number of white squares.

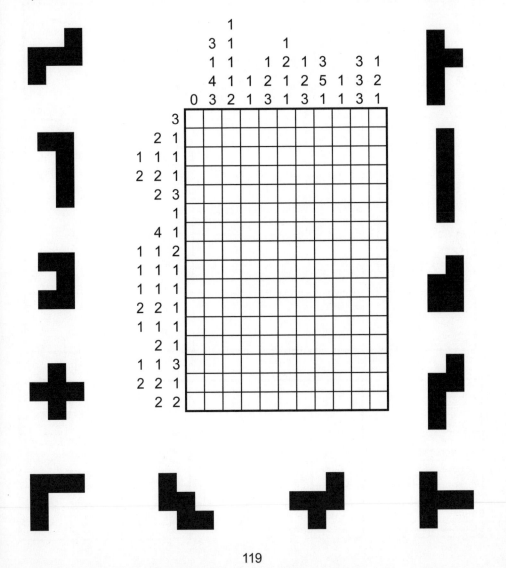

WHERE THE L?

Twelve L-shapes (three pieces of each of the four kinds shown below) need to be inserted in the grid and each L has one hole in it.

Any piece may be turned or flipped over before being put in the grid. No pieces of the same kind touch, even at a corner. The pieces fit together so well that you cannot see any spaces between them; only the holes show. Can you tell where the Ls are?

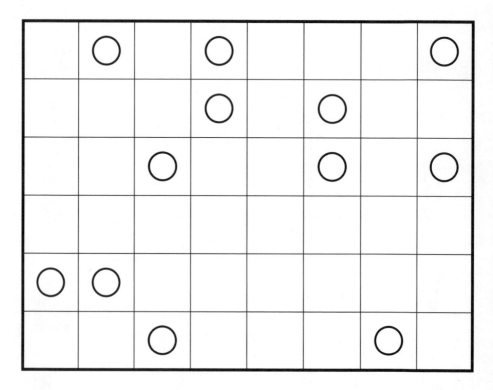

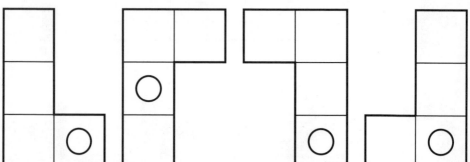

In this puzzle, an amateur coin collector has been out with his metal detector, searching for booty. He didn't have time to dig up all the coins he found, so has made a grid map, showing their locations, in the hope that if he loses the map, at least no-one else will understand it... However, he didn't count on YOU coming across the strange grid (as seen here). Will you be able to discover the correct number of coins and their precise locations?

Those squares containing numbers are empty, but where a number appears in a square, it indicates how many coins are located in the squares (up to a maximum of eight) surrounding the numbered one, touching it at any corner or side. There is only one coin in any individual square.

Place a circle into every square containing a coin.

1		2			2	2	
			4				
	5		3		3		3
		3	1				1
3							1
	1					2	
			1		2		
0		2			3	4	
				3			3
		1			3		
2			2		3	3	
	1			2			

BOX CLEVER

When the box below is folded to form a cube, just one of the five options (A, B, C, D or E) can be produced. Which?

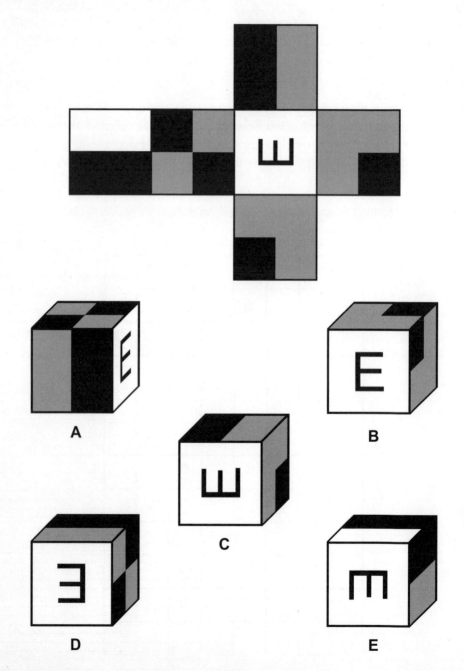

A

B

C

D

E

SYMBOLISM

Each of these squares should contain one or more symbols from the numbered square to the left of its particular horizontal row, plus one or more symbols from the lettered square above its particular vertical column. However, one square doesn't follow this rule. Which is the odd one out?

	A	B	C	D	E	F
	◄ ≈	♣ $	‡ ¿	# ♦	♪ ¶	☼ Σ
1 § Ω	§◄ Ω	§ ♣	§¿ Ω	Ω ♦	¶§	Σ§ ☼
2 ♠ ß	♠ ß	◄ ≈ß	¿♠ ß	♦ß ♠	♠¶	☼♠ ß
3 £ ▶	≈▶ £◄	▶♣ $	¿ £	#£ ▶	£ ♪▶	Σ £☼
4 π ∩	π◄ ≈$	∩π $	‡ π∩	π ∩♦	¶ ∩	☼∩ π
5 ♥ Δ	≈ ♥Δ	♣ Δ♥	Δ‡ ¿	♦# Δ	Δ ¶♥	Σ♥ Δ
6 ▲ ♩	▲ ♩	♩≈ ▲	▲ ♣	‡¿ ♩▲	▲ #♩	♩♪	▲ ♩Σ
7 φ ▼	φ ▼	▼ ◄φ	▼ $	‡▼ ¿	φ #▼	♪ φ	☼ ▼

123

TILE TWISTER

Place the eight tiles into the puzzle grid so that all adjacent numbers on each tile match up. Tiles may be rotated through 360 degrees, but none may be flipped over.

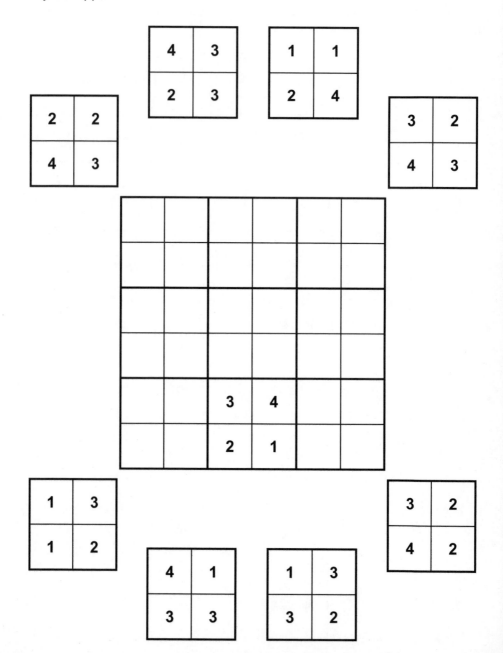

LOGI-6

Every row and column of this grid should contain one each of the letters A, B, C, D, E and F. In addition, each of the six shapes (marked by thicker lines) should also contain one each of the letters A, B, C, D, E and F. Can you complete the grid?

A B C D E F

C				B	A
				D	
			F	E	
	C				
		A			

BATTLESHIPS

Can you place the vessels into the diagram? Some parts of vessels or sea squares have already been filled in. A number to the right or below a row or column refers to the number of occupied squares in that row or column.

Any vessel may be positioned horizontally or vertically, but no part of a vessel touches part of any other vessel, either horizontally, vertically or diagonally.

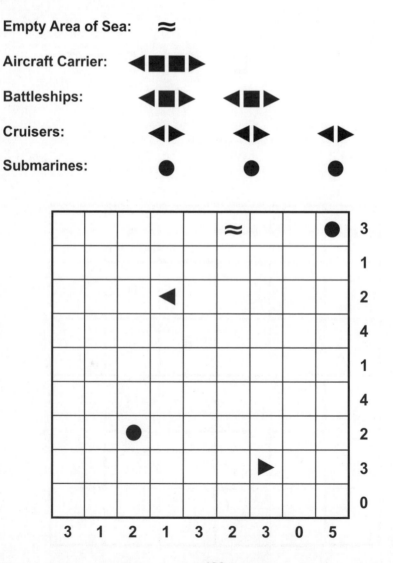

ELIMINATOR

Every oval shape contains a different letter of the alphabet from A to K inclusive. Use the clues to determine their locations. Reference in the clues to 'due' means in any location along the same horizontal or vertical line.

1 A is due north of G, which is due west of E, which is due north of J.

2 I is due east of B, which is next to and north of D.

3 H is next to and north of K, which is due east of G.

4 F is due west of B.

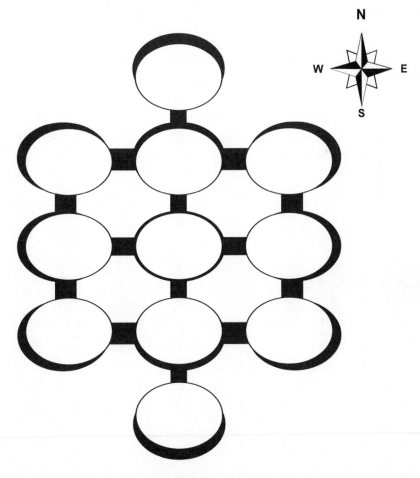

SLITHERLINK

Draw a single continuous loop, by connecting the dots. No line may cross the path of another.

The figure inside each set of any four surrounding dots indicates the total number of surrounding lines.

PIECEWORK

Place all twelve of the pieces into the grid. Any may be rotated or flipped over, but none may touch another, not even diagonally.

The numbers outside the grid refer to the number of consecutive black squares; and each block is separated from the others by at least one white square. For instance, '3 2' could refer to a row with none, one or more white squares, then three black squares, then at least one white square, then two more black squares, followed by any number of white squares.

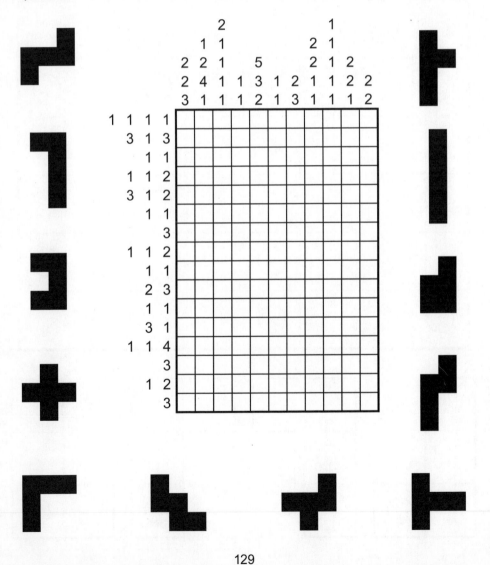

WHERE THE L?

Twelve L-shapes (three pieces of each of the four kinds shown below) need to be inserted in the grid and each L has one hole in it.

Any piece may be turned or flipped over before being put in the grid. No pieces of the same kind touch, even at a corner. The pieces fit together so well that you cannot see any spaces between them; only the holes show. Can you tell where the Ls are?

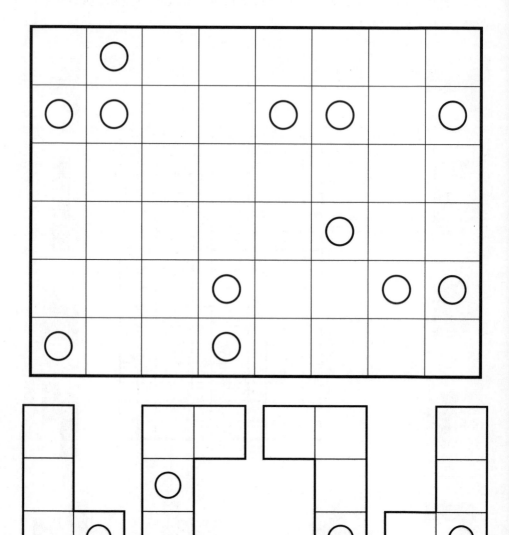

COIN COLLECTING

In this puzzle, an amateur coin collector has been out with his metal detector, searching for booty. He didn't have time to dig up all the coins he found, so has made a grid map, showing their locations, in the hope that if he loses the map, at least no-one else will understand it... However, he didn't count on YOU coming across the strange grid (as seen here). Will you be able to discover the correct number of coins and their precise locations?

Those squares containing numbers are empty, but where a number appears in a square, it indicates how many coins are located in the squares (up to a maximum of eight) surrounding the numbered one, touching it at any corner or side. There is only one coin in any individual square.

Place a circle into every square containing a coin.

1				3	2		0
			3				
	3						
	4	2	2			2	2
		2					
	2		3			3	
			4		5		1
	4						
	4		2				2
						1	
		0		2			0
1							

BOX CLEVER

When the box below is folded to form a cube, just one of the five options (A, B, C, D or E) can be produced. Which?

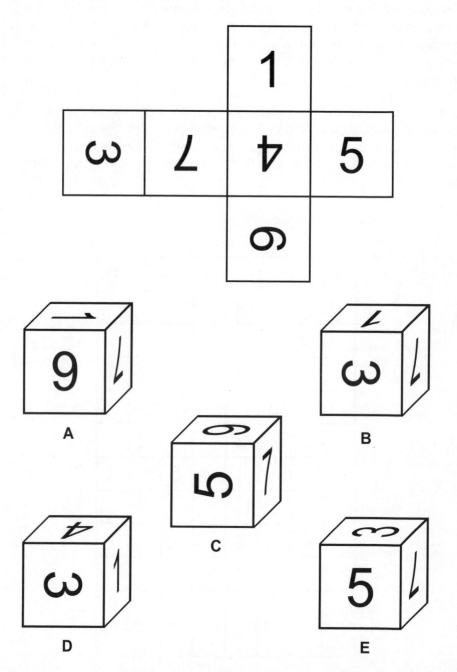

Each of these squares should contain one or more symbols from the numbered square to the left of its particular horizontal row, plus one or more symbols from the lettered square above its particular vertical column. However, one square doesn't follow this rule. Which is the odd one out?

	A	B	C	D	E	F
	◀ R	5 $	‡ L	Σ 2	F ¶	♦ A
1 3 §	◀ §	$§ 35	3§ ‡L	Σ §3	¶ 3F	3 A♦
2 ♠ C	C ◀	5$ ♠C	C♠ L‡	Σ♠ 2C	FC ♠	♦A C♠
3 Δ M	◀Δ M	$M Δ5	L MΔ	2 ΔM	MΔ F	Δ M♦
4 ▼ P	P◀ ▼	▼$ 5P	‡ P	PΣ ▼	P▼ F	▼P ♦
5 K ▶	K◀ ▶	5 ▶K	‡L K▶	K▶ 2	F¶ ▶	A♦ ▶K
6 ▲ 6	◀ 6	6▲ 5	‡ ▲6	Σ6 ▲2	F▲ 6¶	♦ 6A
7 ∩ 0	◀0 ∩	0∩ $	‡ L	Σ∩ 20	¶∩ F0	A♦ 0∩

TILE TWISTER

Place the eight tiles into the puzzle grid so that all adjacent numbers on each tile match up. Tiles may be rotated through 360 degrees, but none may be flipped over.

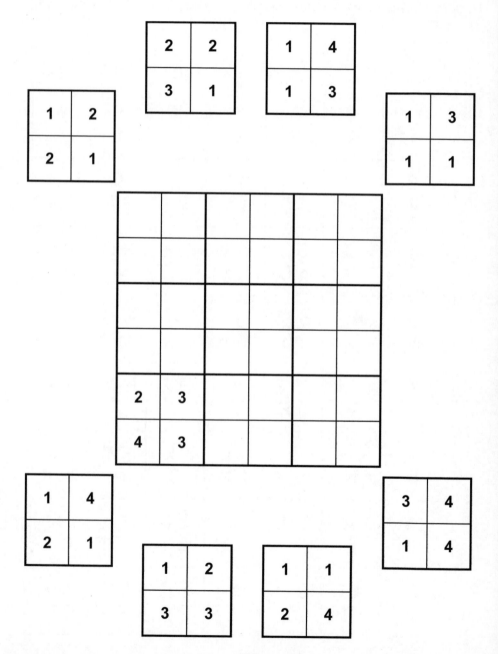

Every row and column of this grid should contain one each of the letters A, B, C, D, E and F. In addition, each of the six shapes (marked by thicker lines) should also contain one each of the letters A, B, C, D, E and F. Can you complete the grid?

A B C D E F

				C	
		B			A
	C				
D					
			F		
F	E				

BATTLESHIPS

Can you place the vessels into the diagram? Some parts of vessels or sea squares have already been filled in. A number to the right or below a row or column refers to the number of occupied squares in that row or column.

Any vessel may be positioned horizontally or vertically, but no part of a vessel touches part of any other vessel, either horizontally, vertically or diagonally.

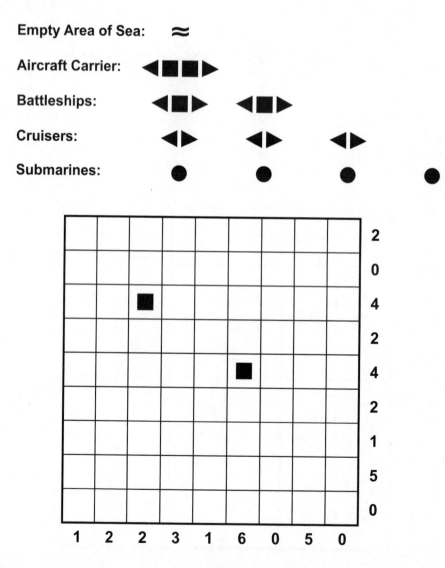

Every oval shape contains a different letter of the alphabet from A to K inclusive. Use the clues to determine their locations. Reference in the clues to 'due' means in any location along the same horizontal or vertical line.

1 K is due south of F, which is next to and west of G.
2 A is due north of H, which is due west of C, which is due south of G.
3 D is due north of J, which is next to and east of E.
4 K is further north than I, but further south than B.
5 A is further north than B, but further south than D. D is not due north of A.

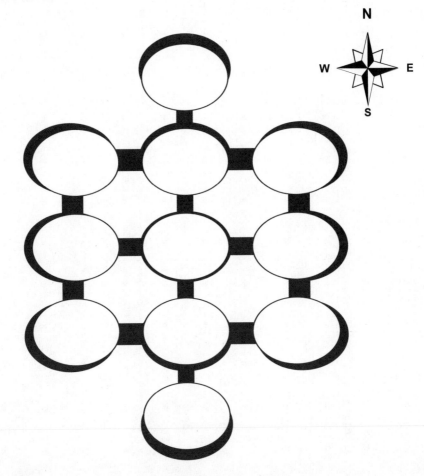

SLITHERLINK

Draw a single continuous loop, by connecting the dots. No line may cross the path of another.

The figure inside each set of any four surrounding dots indicates the total number of surrounding lines.

```
. . . . . . . . . . . .
  1   2       2       1           2
. . . . . . . . . . . .
  1   3   2   2       1       3   1           1
. . . . . . . . . . . .
  1                   1   0       0
. . . . . . . . . . . .
      3                       1           1   2
. . . . . . . . . . . .
      2   2   2   2       2   1       3
. . . . . . . . . . . .
              2       3               1   3
. . . . . . . . . . . .
                      1       1   1       2
. . . . . . . . . . . .
    2       1           2                 1
. . . . . . . . . . . .
    0       1           2       3   2       2
. . . . . . . . . . . .
                        3   2       2
. . . . . . . . . . . .
      2   3   1   0       0   1           1
. . . . . . . . . . . .
    2           3   1           0   0   1
. . . . . . . . . . . .
      2               1   2           2       1
. . . . . . . . . . . .
```

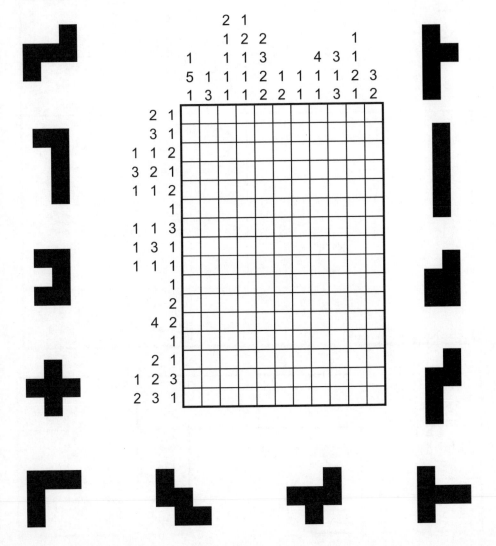

Place all twelve of the pieces into the grid. Any may be rotated or flipped over, but none may touch another, not even diagonally.

The numbers outside the grid refer to the number of consecutive black squares; and each block is separated from the others by at least one white square. For instance, '3 2' could refer to a row with none, one or more white squares, then three black squares, then at least one white square, then two more black squares, followed by any number of white squares.

WHERE THE L?

Twelve L-shapes (three pieces of each of the four kinds shown below) need to be inserted in the grid and each L has one hole in it.

Any piece may be turned or flipped over before being put in the grid. No pieces of the same kind touch, even at a corner. The pieces fit together so well that you cannot see any spaces between them; only the holes show. Can you tell where the Ls are?

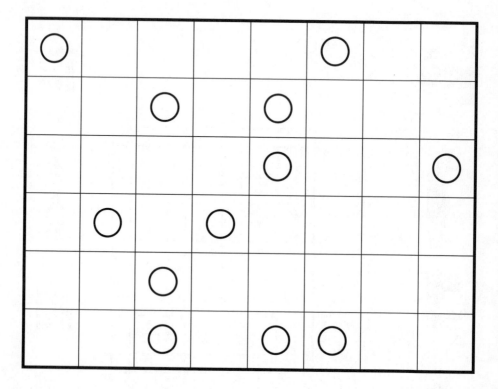

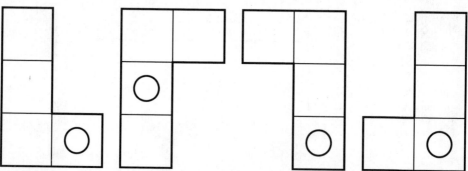

In this puzzle, an amateur coin collector has been out with his metal detector, searching for booty. He didn't have time to dig up all the coins he found, so has made a grid map, showing their locations, in the hope that if he loses the map, at least no-one else will understand it... However, he didn't count on YOU coming across the strange grid (as seen here). Will you be able to discover the correct number of coins and their precise locations?

Those squares containing numbers are empty, but where a number appears in a square, it indicates how many coins are located in the squares (up to a maximum of eight) surrounding the numbered one, touching it at any corner or side. There is only one coin in any individual square.

Place a circle into every square containing a coin.

				2	2		1
	2	0					
	1	1		1	2		2
				1		3	
		2	1		1		2
	3			4			
1							2
		6			3		
				3	0		
	2		5			1	
2				1	1		

BOX CLEVER

When the box below is folded to form a cube, just one of the five options (A, B, C, D or E) can be produced. Which?

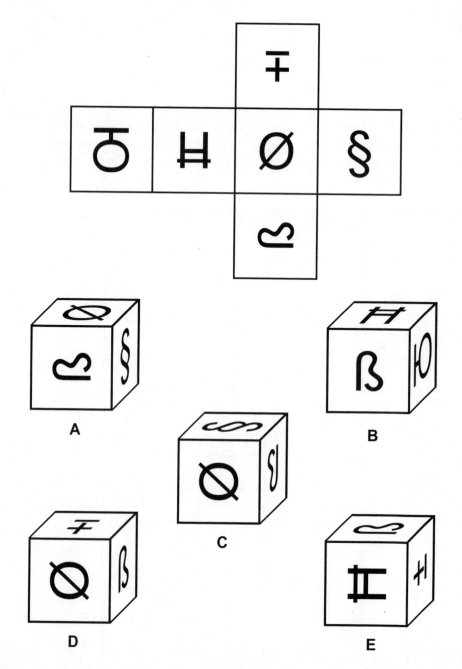

Each of these squares should contain one or more symbols from the numbered square to the left of its particular horizontal row, plus one or more symbols from the lettered square above its particular vertical column. However, one square doesn't follow this rule. Which is the odd one out?

	A	B	C	D	E	F
	Ө Π	€ $	‡ ©	◆ #	♪ µ	Σ ♂
1 ∩ π	Π Ө∩	π∩ $€	π‡ ©	◆∩	♪µ ∩	π ♂
2 ♠ Ψ	♠Π Ψ	$ ♠	♠ ©	Ψ#	♠µ	Ψ Σ♠
3 £ ►	Ө Π£	►$ £	‡£	◆# ►	µ ►♪	£Σ ♂
4 Ю §	ӨΠ Ю	§ €$	© Ю‡	#Ю	♪§	ΣЮ §
5 Δ א	א ΠΔ	א€ §$	© ‡Δ	◆א #	Δ♪	♂ ΣΔ
6 ▲ ٩	Ө ▲٩	€ ٩	٩ ▲‡	٩# ◆	µ▲ ♪	٩Σ
7 ▼ Я	ЯΠ	€Я	Я ‡©	#Я	♪ ▼	▼ Σ♂

TILE TWISTER

Place the eight tiles into the puzzle grid so that all adjacent numbers on each tile match up. Tiles may be rotated through 360 degrees, but none may be flipped over.

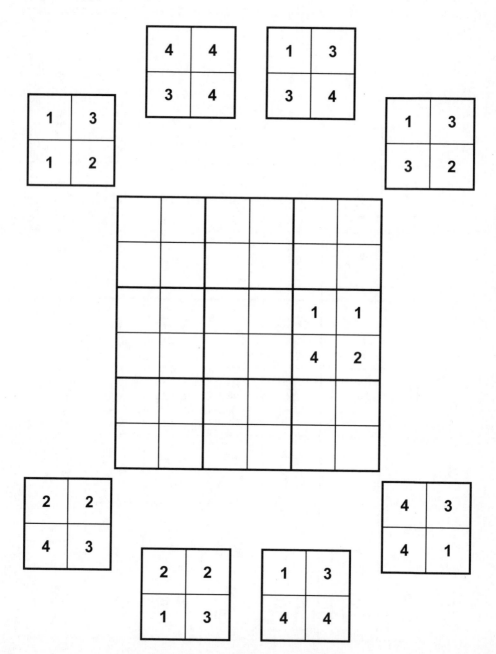

Every row and column of this grid should contain one each of the letters A, B, C, D, E and F. In addition, each of the six shapes (marked by thicker lines) should also contain one each of the letters A, B, C, D, E and F. Can you complete the grid?

A   B   C   D   E   F

	C			B	A
E					
				D	
	F			E	
			F		

BATTLESHIPS

Can you place the vessels into the diagram? Some parts of vessels or sea squares have already been filled in. A number to the right or below a row or column refers to the number of occupied squares in that row or column.

Any vessel may be positioned horizontally or vertically, but no part of a vessel touches part of any other vessel, either horizontally, vertically or diagonally.

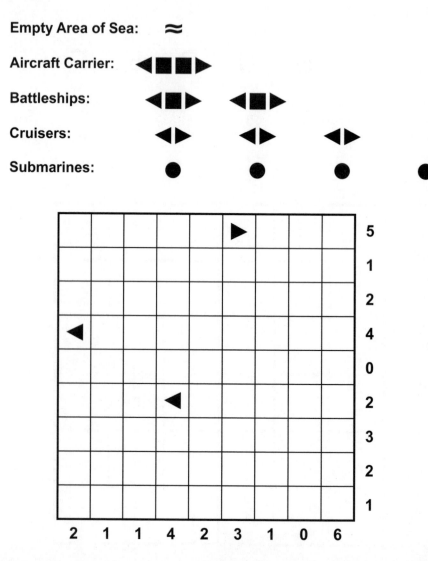

Every oval shape contains a different letter of the alphabet from A to K inclusive. Use the clues to determine their locations. Reference in the clues to 'due' means in any location along the same horizontal or vertical line.

1 F is next to and east of I, which is next to and north of A.

2 D is next to and south of H, which is further west than A.

3 K is due west of C, which is due north of G.

4 E is next to and north of B.

5 H is further north than J, but further south than K.

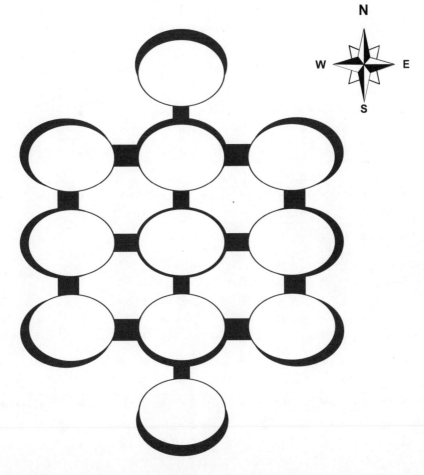

SLITHERLINK

Draw a single continuous loop, by connecting the dots. No line may cross the path of another.

The figure inside each set of any four surrounding dots indicates the total number of surrounding lines.

PIECEWORK

Place all twelve of the pieces into the grid. Any may be rotated or flipped over, but none may touch another, not even diagonally.

The numbers outside the grid refer to the number of consecutive black squares; and each block is separated from the others by at least one white square. For instance, '3 2' could refer to a row with none, one or more white squares, then three black squares, then at least one white square, then two more black squares, followed by any number of white squares.

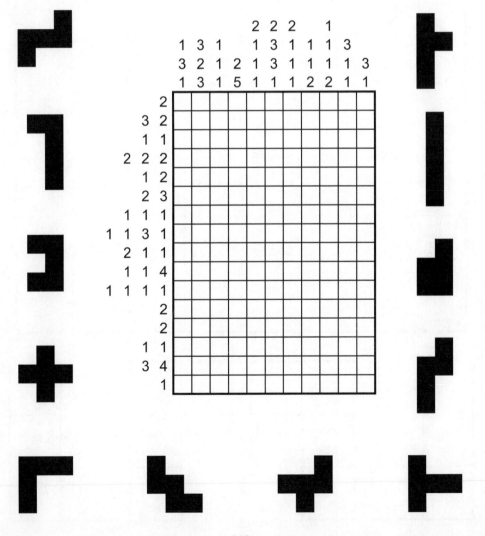

WHERE THE L?

Twelve L-shapes (three pieces of each of the four kinds shown below) need to be inserted in the grid and each L has one hole in it.

Any piece may be turned or flipped over before being put in the grid. No pieces of the same kind touch, even at a corner. The pieces fit together so well that you cannot see any spaces between them; only the holes show. Can you tell where the Ls are?

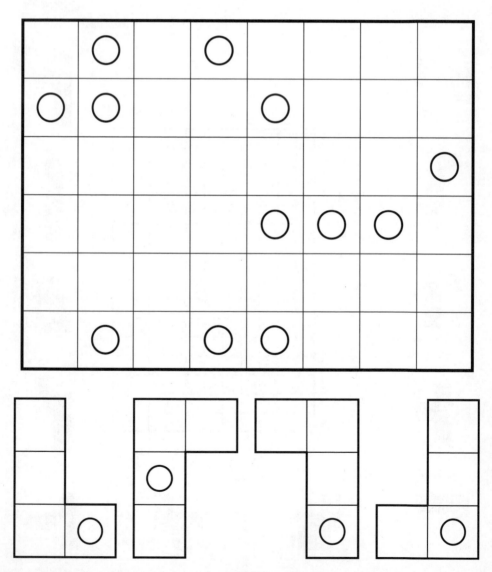

In this puzzle, an amateur coin collector has been out with his metal detector, searching for booty. He didn't have time to dig up all the coins he found, so has made a grid map, showing their locations, in the hope that if he loses the map, at least no-one else will understand it... However, he didn't count on YOU coming across the strange grid (as seen here). Will you be able to discover the correct number of coins and their precise locations?

Those squares containing numbers are empty, but where a number appears in a square, it indicates how many coins are located in the squares (up to a maximum of eight) surrounding the numbered one, touching it at any corner or side. There is only one coin in any individual square.

Place a circle into every square containing a coin.

1		2			1		
			3				2
		3	3				
0				3			3
	0		3			2	
		2		4			0
	3						
3							1
			2	2		4	
	2	1			4		4
			1				
	0	1				3	

BOX CLEVER

When the box below is folded to form a cube, just one of the five options (A, B, C, D or E) can be produced. Which?

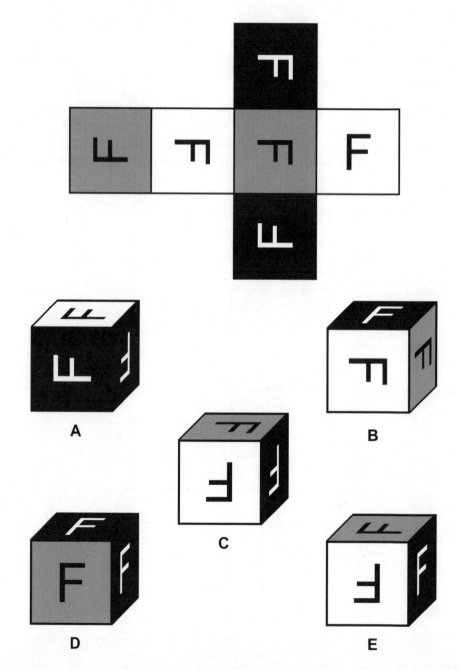

Each of these squares should contain one or more symbols from the numbered square to the left of its particular horizontal row, plus one or more symbols from the lettered square above its particular vertical column. However, one square doesn't follow this rule. Which is the odd one out?

	A	B	C	D	E	F
	= ¥	Э ⇧	▲ ▼	μ ♀	♪ ∏	‡ θ
1 $ ¿	¿= $¥	$ ⇧Э	¿▲ ▼$	$¿ ♀μ	¿$ ∏♪	‡ θ¿
2 ◄ ß	= ß◄	ß	◄ß ◄⇧	♀μ ß	♪ ◄ß	◄θ ‡
3 £ ►	£ ►	£ ¥►	►Э ⇧	►▼ ▲	►♀ £μ	►£ ∏	θ‡ £►
4 Ω §	Ω §	¥= §	⇧Э Ω§	§Ω ▼▲	♀ μ§	§ Ω♪	θΩ §
5 ♪ ¶	♪ ¶	♪ =¥	Э¶ ♪⇧	▼▲ ♪¶	♀μ §♪	¶ ∏	♪ ‡θ
6 ▲ Σ	▲ Σ	¥ ▲	▲Э Σ⇧	Σ▼ ▲	μΣ ▲♀	▲Σ ∏♪	Σ▲ θ‡
7 ℓ #	ℓ #	ℓ ¥	Эℓ ⇧#	ℓ ▲	♀# ℓμ	♪∏ #ℓ	ℓ# θ‡

153

TILE TWISTER

Place the eight tiles into the puzzle grid so that all adjacent numbers on each tile match up. Tiles may be rotated through 360 degrees, but none may be flipped over.

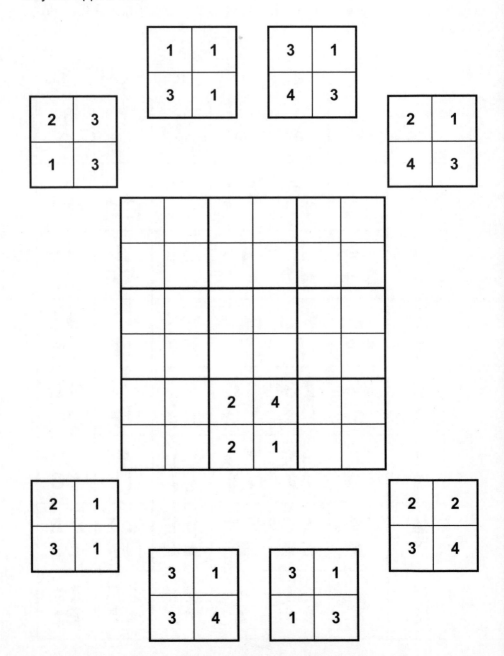

Every row and column of this grid should contain one each of the letters A, B, C, D, E and F. In addition, each of the six shapes (marked by thicker lines) should also contain one each of the letters A, B, C, D, E and F. Can you complete the grid?

A B C D E F

	E			F	
		D			
					A
			C		
	A		B		

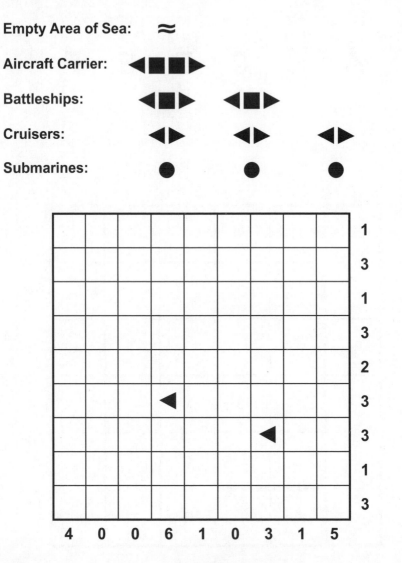

BATTLESHIPS

Can you place the vessels into the diagram? Some parts of vessels or sea squares have already been filled in. A number to the right or below a row or column refers to the number of occupied squares in that row or column.

Any vessel may be positioned horizontally or vertically, but no part of a vessel touches part of any other vessel, either horizontally, vertically or diagonally.

Empty Area of Sea: ≈

Aircraft Carrier:

Battleships:

Cruisers:

Submarines:

Every oval shape contains a different letter of the alphabet from A to K inclusive. Use the clues to determine their locations. Reference in the clues to 'due' means in any location along the same horizontal or vertical line.

1 B is next to and west of G, which is due north of C, which is due south of D.

2 J is next to and east of A, which is due south of H, which is further north than D.

3 E is due west of F, which is next to and north of I, which is due north of J.

4 A is next to and south of G, which is further north than K.

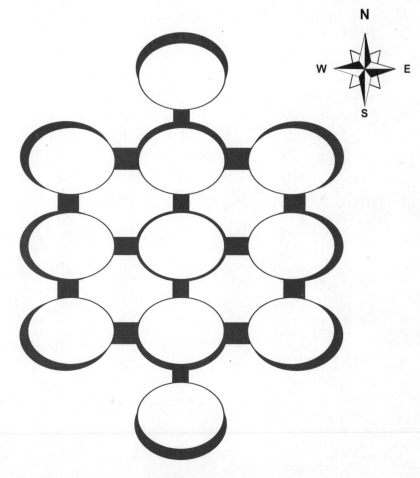

SLITHERLINK

Draw a single continuous loop, by connecting the dots. No line may cross the path of another.

The figure inside each set of any four surrounding dots indicates the total number of surrounding lines.

Place all twelve of the pieces into the grid. Any may be rotated or flipped over, but none may touch another, not even diagonally.

The numbers outside the grid refer to the number of consecutive black squares; and each block is separated from the others by at least one white square. For instance, '3 2' could refer to a row with none, one or more white squares, then three black squares, then at least one white square, then two more black squares, followed by any number of white squares.

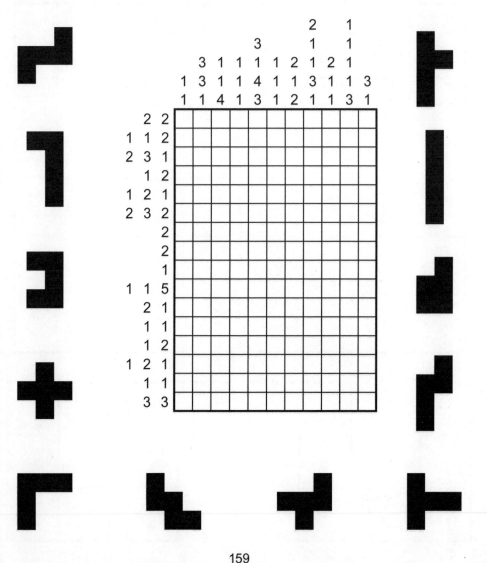

WHERE THE L?

Twelve L-shapes (three pieces of each of the four kinds shown below) need to be inserted in the grid and each L has one hole in it.

Any piece may be turned or flipped over before being put in the grid. No pieces of the same kind touch, even at a corner. The pieces fit together so well that you cannot see any spaces between them; only the holes show. Can you tell where the Ls are?

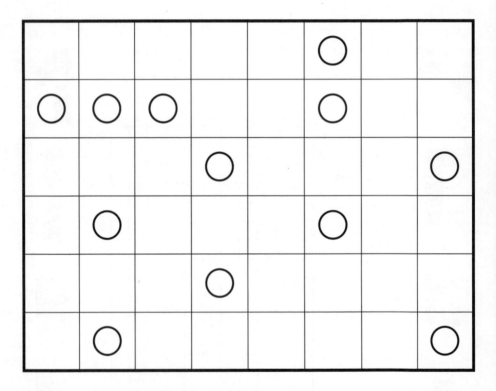

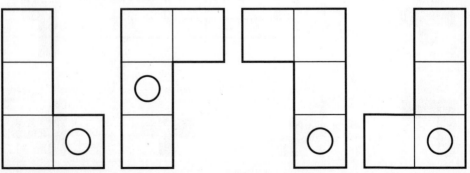

In this puzzle, an amateur coin collector has been out with his metal detector, searching for booty. He didn't have time to dig up all the coins he found, so has made a grid map, showing their locations, in the hope that if he loses the map, at least no-one else will understand it... However, he didn't count on YOU coming across the strange grid (as seen here). Will you be able to discover the correct number of coins and their precise locations?

Those squares containing numbers are empty, but where a number appears in a square, it indicates how many coins are located in the squares (up to a maximum of eight) surrounding the numbered one, touching it at any corner or side. There is only one coin in any individual square.

Place a circle into every square containing a coin.

0	1			0			1
	1	1			3		
						0	
3		2				1	
	4	3	1	1			
			2	2			
	4	3		1		1	
			4	2			
	4	2			2		
	2	1				1	
	2			2			

BOX CLEVER

When the box below is folded to form a cube, just one of the five options (A, B, C, D or E) can be produced. Which?

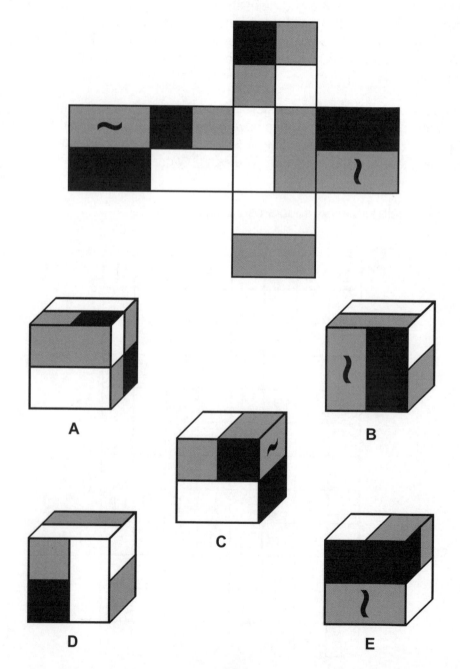

Each of these squares should contain one or more symbols from the numbered square to the left of its particular horizontal row, plus one or more symbols from the lettered square above its particular vertical column. However, one square doesn't follow this rule. Which is the odd one out?

	A	B	C	D	E	F
	◄ ₪	⚹ $	‡ »	♦ #	♪ ±	Σ ⇧
1	≠ π	₪ ≠ ◄	≠ π ⚹	π ‡ ≠	# π ≠ ♦	± ≠	Σ ≠ π
2	♠ Θ	Θ ₪	$ Θ ♠	» Θ	♠ #	Θ ♠ ♪	Σ ♠
3	• ▶	◄ ▶	• ▶ ⚹ $	▶ ‡ »	♦ •	• ♪ ±	⇧ ▶ •
4	Ω §	₪ Ω	§ $	Ω » §	# Ω	§ ± ♪	Ω ⇧ Σ
5	Δ ♥	◄ ₪ Δ	⚹ Δ $	♥ »	Δ ♦ #	± ♪ Δ ♥	Σ Δ ⇧
6	▲ †	† ◄	$ ⚹ ▲	‡ » † ▲	♦ † #	▲ † ♪ ±	▲ ⇧
7	▼ π	₪ ▼ ◄	$ ▼ π	▼ » ‡	π # ♦ ▼	π ± ▼	▼ ▲ ⇧

163

TILE TWISTER

Place the eight tiles into the puzzle grid so that all adjacent numbers on each tile match up. Tiles may be rotated through 360 degrees, but none may be flipped over.

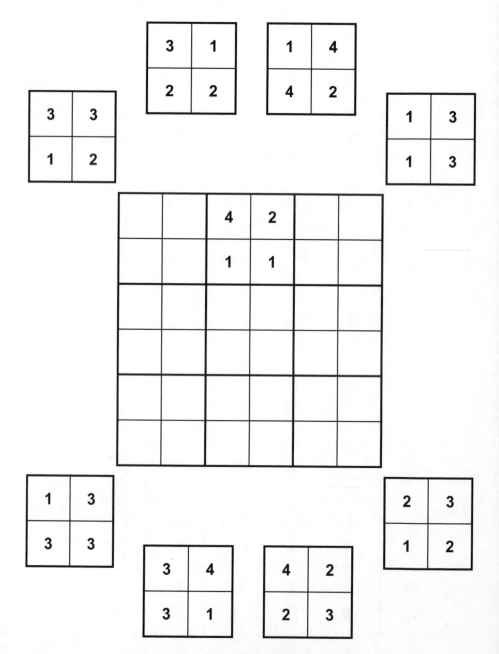

LOGI-6

Every row and column of this grid should contain one each of the letters A, B, C, D, E and F. In addition, each of the six shapes (marked by thicker lines) should also contain one each of the letters A, B, C, D, E and F. Can you complete the grid?

A B C D E F

			C	B	A
	D				
					E
				F	
B					

BATTLESHIPS

Can you place the vessels into the diagram? Some parts of vessels or sea squares have already been filled in. A number to the right or below a row or column refers to the number of occupied squares in that row or column.

Any vessel may be positioned horizontally or vertically, but no part of a vessel touches part of any other vessel, either horizontally, vertically or diagonally.

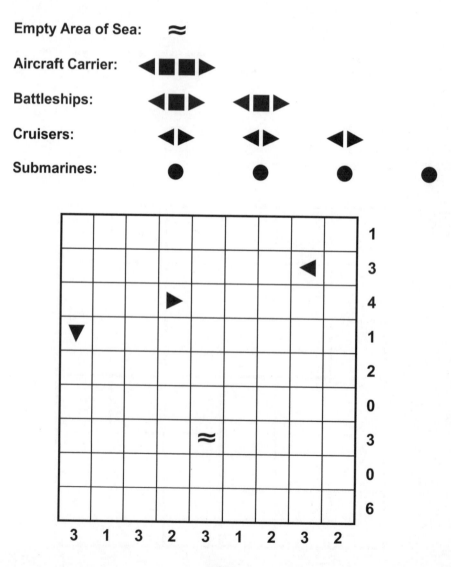

Every oval shape contains a different letter of the alphabet from A to K inclusive. Use the clues to determine their locations. Reference in the clues to 'due' means in any location along the same horizontal or vertical line.

1 G is next to and north of J, which is next to and east of I.
2 H is next to and north of E, which is next to and west of B.
3 B is due south of F, which is next to and east of D.
4 K is further south than C, but further north than A.
5 A is further west than J, which is further north than E.

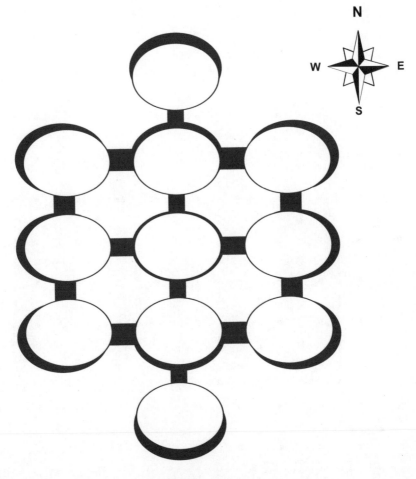

SLITHERLINK

Draw a single continuous loop, by connecting the dots. No line may cross the path of another.

The figure inside each set of any four surrounding dots indicates the total number of surrounding lines.

PIECEWORK

Place all twelve of the pieces into the grid. Any may be rotated or flipped over, but none may touch another, not even diagonally.

The numbers outside the grid refer to the number of consecutive black squares; and each block is separated from the others by at least one white square. For instance, '3 2' could refer to a row with none, one or more white squares, then three black squares, then at least one white square, then two more black squares, followed by any number of white squares.

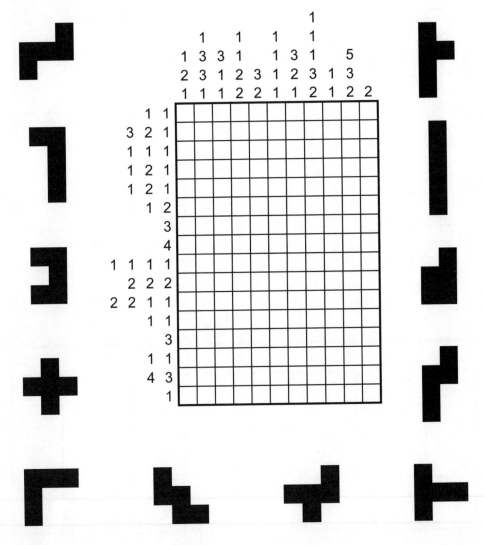

WHERE THE L?

Twelve L-shapes (three pieces of each of the four kinds shown below) need to be inserted in the grid and each L has one hole in it.

Any piece may be turned or flipped over before being put in the grid. No pieces of the same kind touch, even at a corner. The pieces fit together so well that you cannot see any spaces between them; only the holes show. Can you tell where the Ls are?

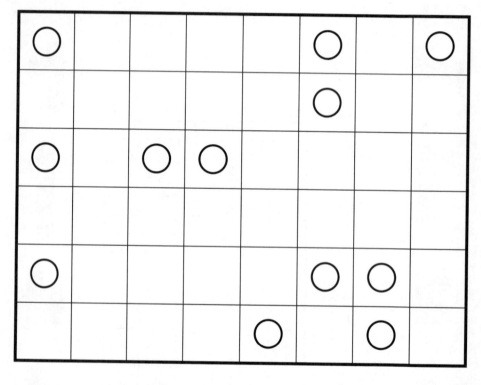

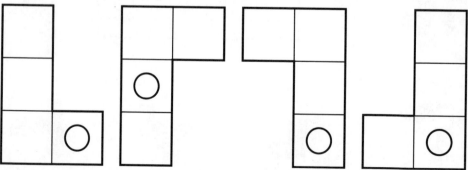

COIN COLLECTING

In this puzzle, an amateur coin collector has been out with his metal detector, searching for booty. He didn't have time to dig up all the coins he found, so has made a grid map, showing their locations, in the hope that if he loses the map, at least no-one else will understand it... However, he didn't count on YOU coming across the strange grid (as seen here). Will you be able to discover the correct number of coins and their precise locations?

Those squares containing numbers are empty, but where a number appears in a square, it indicates how many coins are located in the squares (up to a maximum of eight) surrounding the numbered one, touching it at any corner or side. There is only one coin in any individual square.

Place a circle into every square containing a coin.

	3						
2				3		0	
3				1			
			2	2		1	
2		2			1		
		2		1		3	3
		1			3		
1	1					5	
3				3			
			3		2		
				2	1		1
	1				1	0	

BOX CLEVER

When the box below is folded to form a cube, just one of the five options (A, B, C, D or E) can be produced. Which?

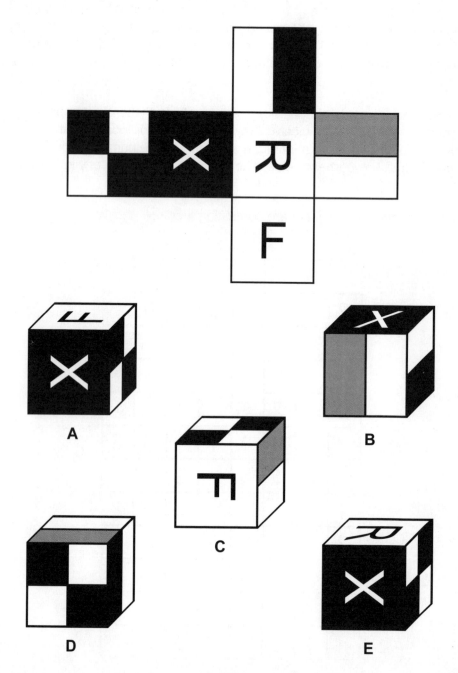

Each of these squares should contain one or more symbols from the numbered square to the left of its particular horizontal row, plus one or more symbols from the lettered square above its particular vertical column. However, one square doesn't follow this rule. Which is the odd one out?

	A	B	C	D	E	F
	◄ £	T $	H &	♦ π	♪ ¶	Σ L
1 8 #	8 £ ◄	T # $	& H 8	8 π ♦	♪ ¶ #	Σ # L
2 Z ß	Z ß ◄	ß T Z	H ß	π Z ♦	ß ♪ ¶	L Z Σ
3 ¿ ►	¿ ► £ ◄	► $ T	H ¿ ►	♦ ► ¿ π	¿ ► ♪	L ► ¿
4 Ω §	◄ Ω §	T $ Ω	§ Ω &	π ♦ Ω §	§ Ω ¶	§ L
5 B 4	B ◄ 4 £	4 $ B	4 H &	π 4 ♦	¶ 4 B	4 B Σ L
6 ▲ U	U ◄ £	U ▲ $ T	& ▲ H	♦ U π	♪ ▲ U	Σ U
7 ▼ φ	◄ φ ▼	φ ▼	& ▼ φ	♦ φ	▼ ¶ ♪	φ ▼ L

173

TILE TWISTER

Place the eight tiles into the puzzle grid so that all adjacent numbers on each tile match up. Tiles may be rotated through 360 degrees, but none may be flipped over.

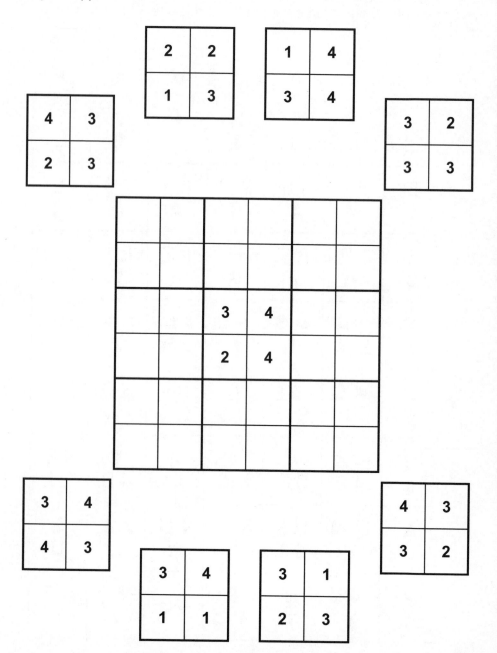

Every row and column of this grid should contain one each of the letters A, B, C, D, E and F. In addition, each of the six shapes (marked by thicker lines) should also contain one each of the letters A, B, C, D, E and F. Can you complete the grid?

A B C D E F

BATTLESHIPS

Can you place the vessels into the diagram? Some parts of vessels or sea squares have already been filled in. A number to the right or below a row or column refers to the number of occupied squares in that row or column.

Any vessel may be positioned horizontally or vertically, but no part of a vessel touches part of any other vessel, either horizontally, vertically or diagonally.

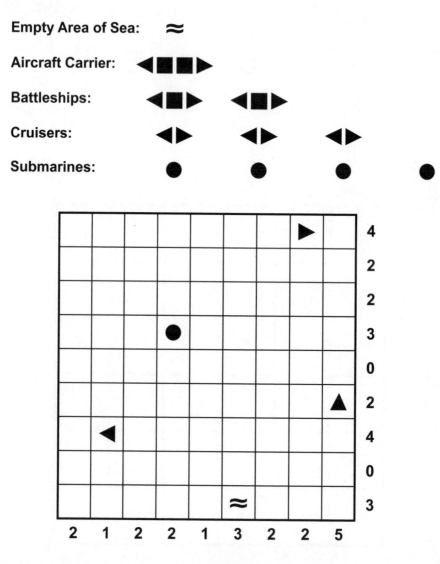

Every oval shape contains a different letter of the alphabet from A to K inclusive. Use the clues to determine their locations. Reference in the clues to 'due' means in any location along the same horizontal or vertical line.

1 B is next to and west of G, which is next to and north of H.

2 C is due west of H, which is next to and north of F.

3 D is further north than A, which is due north of B.

4 E is next to and west of I, which is next to and north of J, which is next to and north of D.

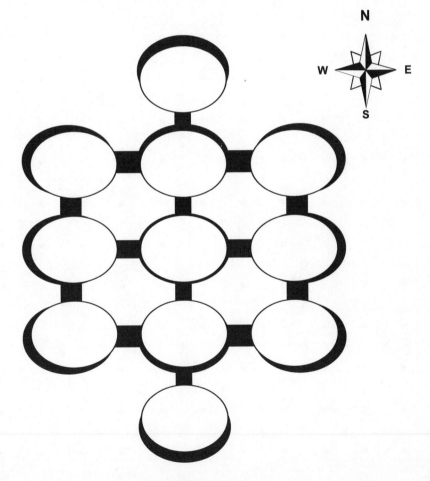

SLITHERLINK

Draw a single continuous loop, by connecting the dots. No line may cross the path of another.

The figure inside each set of any four surrounding dots indicates the total number of surrounding lines.

```
·    ·    ·    ·    ·    ·    ·    ·    ·    ·    ·    ·
   2    1    2    2              3    1
·    ·    ·    ·    ·    ·    ·    ·    ·    ·    ·    ·
   3    1    0                             0    2
·    ·    ·    ·    ·    ·    ·    ·    ·    ·    ·    ·
        1         1              0    1
·    ·    ·    ·    ·    ·    ·    ·    ·    ·    ·    ·
   3                   1         3
·    ·    ·    ·    ·    ·    ·    ·    ·    ·    ·    ·
 1              1    0    1    2
·    ·    ·    ·    ·    ·    ·    ·    ·    ·    ·    ·
 1                   2         3              1
·    ·    ·    ·    ·    ·    ·    ·    ·    ·    ·    ·
        1                   1    2    1
·    ·    ·    ·    ·    ·    ·    ·    ·    ·    ·    ·
 1         0    1    1    2    3         2
·    ·    ·    ·    ·    ·    ·    ·    ·    ·    ·    ·
   1    0                   1
·    ·    ·    ·    ·    ·    ·    ·    ·    ·    ·    ·
        1
·    ·    ·    ·    ·    ·    ·    ·    ·    ·    ·    ·
 3    1    0         0    1    1         3
·    ·    ·    ·    ·    ·    ·    ·    ·    ·    ·    ·
             1         3
·    ·    ·    ·    ·    ·    ·    ·    ·    ·    ·    ·
 3    2    3    2
·    ·    ·    ·    ·    ·    ·    ·    ·    ·    ·    ·
```

PIECEWORK

Place all twelve of the pieces into the grid. Any may be rotated or flipped over, but none may touch another, not even diagonally.

The numbers outside the grid refer to the number of consecutive black squares; and each block is separated from the others by at least one white square. For instance, '3 2' could refer to a row with none, one or more white squares, then three black squares, then at least one white square, then two more black squares, followed by any number of white squares.

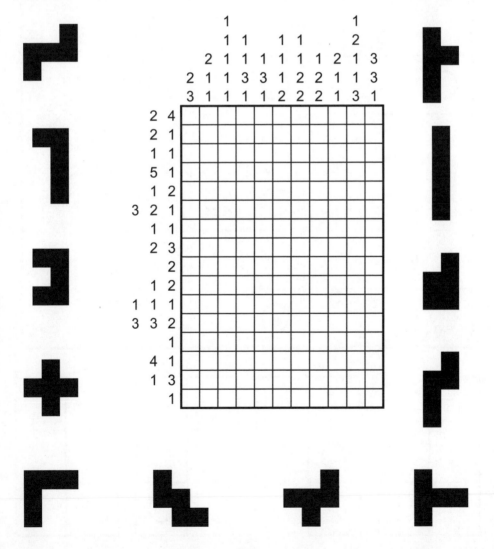

WHERE THE L?

Twelve L-shapes (three pieces of each of the four kinds shown below) need to be inserted in the grid and each L has one hole in it.

Any piece may be turned or flipped over before being put in the grid. No pieces of the same kind touch, even at a corner. The pieces fit together so well that you cannot see any spaces between them; only the holes show. Can you tell where the Ls are?

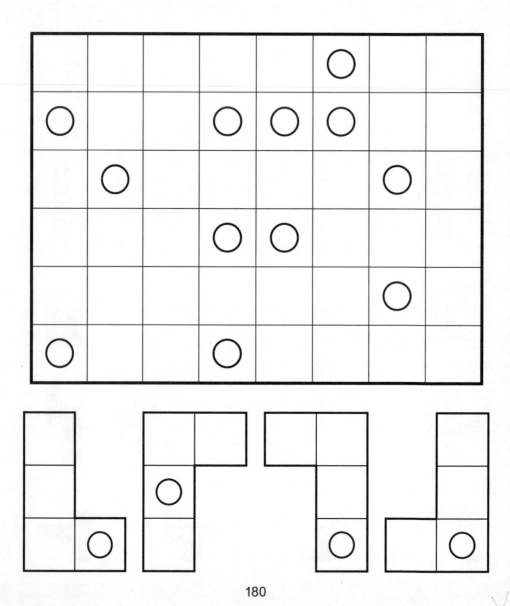

In this puzzle, an amateur coin collector has been out with his metal detector, searching for booty. He didn't have time to dig up all the coins he found, so has made a grid map, showing their locations, in the hope that if he loses the map, at least no-one else will understand it... However, he didn't count on YOU coming across the strange grid (as seen here). Will you be able to discover the correct number of coins and their precise locations?

Those squares containing numbers are empty, but where a number appears in a square, it indicates how many coins are located in the squares (up to a maximum of eight) surrounding the numbered one, touching it at any corner or side. There is only one coin in any individual square.

Place a circle into every square containing a coin.

1			1		3		
							2
	1	2		3	4		
		3					
			1			2	
3	4		4				3
					3		3
3			4				
2					2		3
	4					3	
			1		1		1
	0						

BOX CLEVER

When the box below is folded to form a cube, just one of the five options (A, B, C, D or E) can be produced. Which?

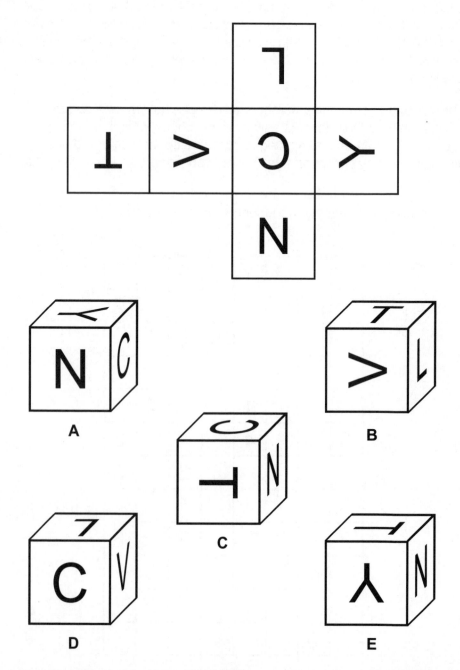

Each of these squares should contain one or more symbols from the numbered square to the left of its particular horizontal row, plus one or more symbols from the lettered square above its particular vertical column. However, one square doesn't follow this rule. Which is the odd one out?

	A	B	C	D	E	F
	◄ R	2 $	‡ 6	8 #	♪ J	Σ F
1	∩ L	∩ L◄	L2 $	L6 ‡∩	# 8∩	♪L	Σ ∩L
2	C ß	◄ß C	2$ ß	C 6	C# 8	ßC ♪	F Cß
3	V ►	►◄	$► V	‡ ►V	V►	VJ	VF Σ
4	Ω 9	◄9 R	9 2	Ω9 ‡	#9 8	J♪ Ω	9 FΩ
5	Δ 4	ΔR	2 4$	4Δ 6	8Δ 4#	Δ J4	Σ4
6	▲ M	R▲ ◄	$ M▲	M6	▲ 8	JM ▲	▲M FΣ
7	▼ Z	◄R ▼	▼2 Z	6▼	8 Z	Z ♪J	ΣZ ▼

TILE TWISTER

Place the eight tiles into the puzzle grid so that all adjacent numbers on each tile match up. Tiles may be rotated through 360 degrees, but none may be flipped over.

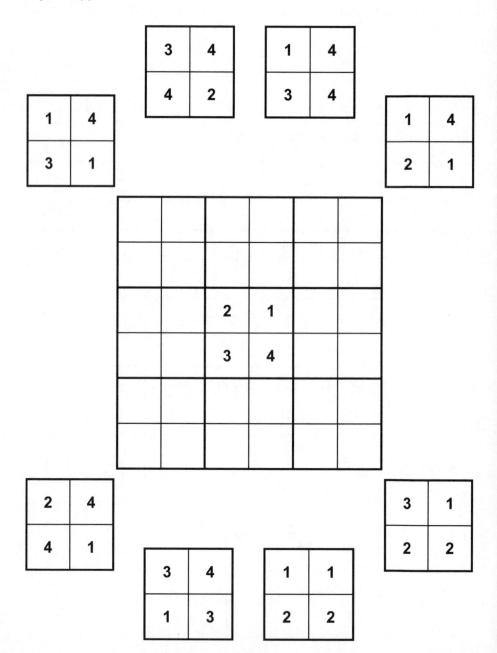

Every row and column of this grid should contain one each of the letters A, B, C, D, E and F. In addition, each of the six shapes (marked by thicker lines) should also contain one each of the letters A, B, C, D, E and F. Can you complete the grid?

A B C D E F

		B			A
		C			
D					
				E	
		E			
	F				

BATTLESHIPS

Can you place the vessels into the diagram? Some parts of vessels or sea squares have already been filled in. A number to the right or below a row or column refers to the number of occupied squares in that row or column.

Any vessel may be positioned horizontally or vertically, but no part of a vessel touches part of any other vessel, either horizontally, vertically or diagonally.

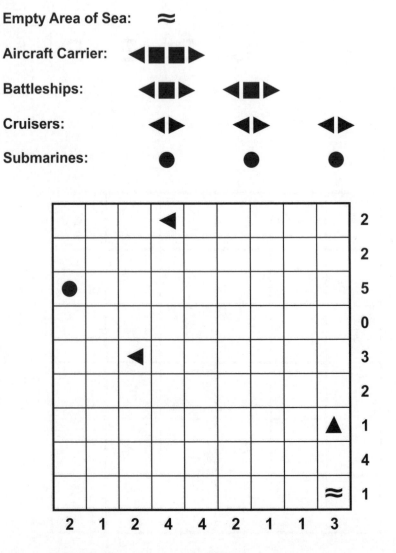

Every oval shape contains a different letter of the alphabet from A to K inclusive. Use the clues to determine their locations. Reference in the clues to 'due' means in any location along the same horizontal or vertical line.

1 A is due east of D, which is due north of B.
2 B is due east of I, which is due south of K.
3 J is next to and north of E, which is both further north and further east than G.
4 G is due south of H, which is due north of B.
5 C is due west of H, which is due south of F.

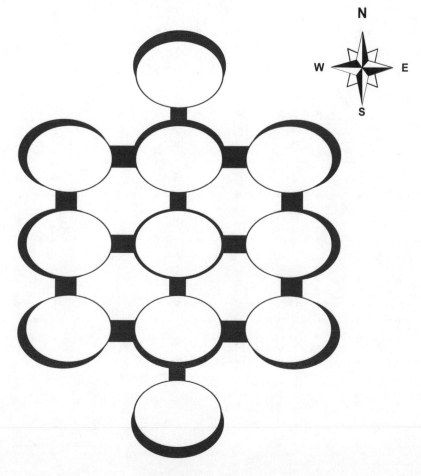

SLITHERLINK

Draw a single continuous loop, by connecting the dots. No line may cross the path of another.

The figure inside each set of any four surrounding dots indicates the total number of surrounding lines.

PIECEWORK

Place all twelve of the pieces into the grid. Any may be rotated or flipped over, but none may touch another, not even diagonally.

The numbers outside the grid refer to the number of consecutive black squares; and each block is separated from the others by at least one white square. For instance, '3 2' could refer to a row with none, one or more white squares, then three black squares, then at least one white square, then two more black squares, followed by any number of white squares.

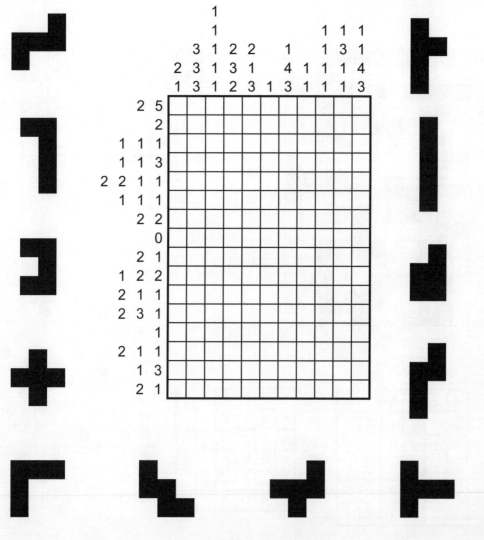

Solutions

1

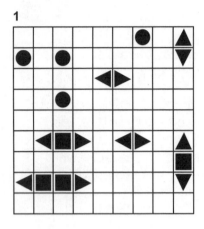

2

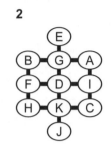

3

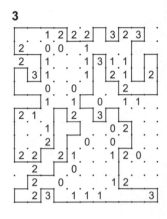

4

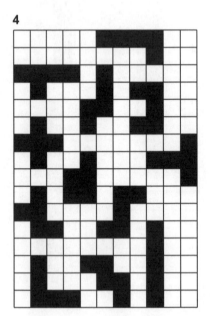

5

7
E

8
F4

6

	1		1	●		0	
1	●	2		2			
		●		1	●		0
●	●	4				2	
	4	●	●				●
0		●			1	3	
		1			1	●	●
●	3		1			3	●
●	●		●	1	1	2	2
●	5					●	
●	●		0		●	●	3
●	3				3	●	

9

2	3	3	3	3	1
1	3	3	4	4	2
1	3	3	4	4	2
2	1	1	2	2	3
2	1	1	2	2	3
4	1	1	4	4	4

10

D	F	B	C	A	E
A	D	E	F	C	B
B	E	C	A	D	F
C	B	F	D	E	A
F	C	A	E	B	D
E	A	D	B	F	C

190

Solutions

11

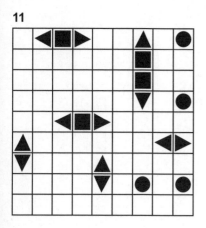

12

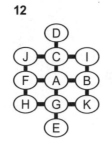

13

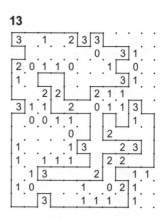

14

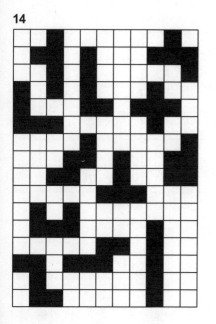

15

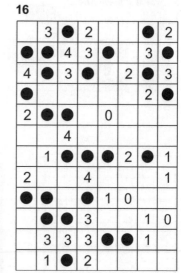

16

17
A

18
E5

19

4	3	3	3	3	4
1	4	4	2	2	2
1	4	4	2	2	2
4	2	2	1	1	3
4	2	2	1	1	3
1	1	1	3	3	3

20

C	F	A	B	D	E
E	B	D	A	F	C
A	E	B	F	C	D
D	A	E	C	B	F
B	C	F	D	E	A
F	D	C	E	A	B

Solutions

21

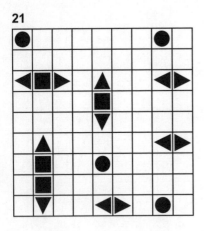

22

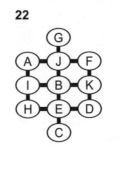

23

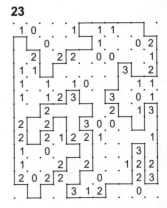

24

25

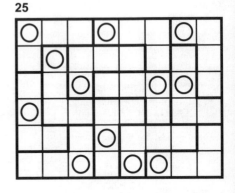

26

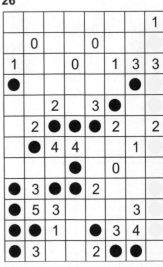

27
E

28
C6

29

1	3	3	4	4	4
3	4	4	1	1	3
3	4	4	1	1	3
4	2	2	3	3	3
4	2	2	3	3	3
1	3	3	1	1	2

30

C	E	D	F	B	A
F	B	E	D	A	C
E	A	C	B	F	D
A	C	F	E	D	B
B	D	A	C	E	F
D	F	B	A	C	E

Solutions

31

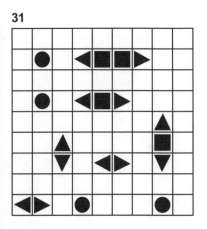

32

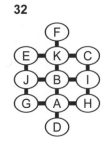

33

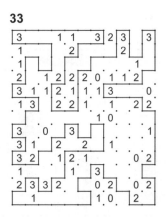

34

35

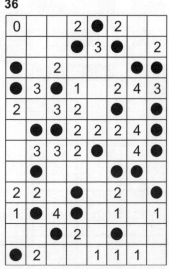

36

37
B

38
E7

39

4	4	4	2	2	1
1	3	3	2	2	1
1	3	3	2	2	1
4	3	3	4	4	1
4	3	3	4	4	1
1	4	4	2	2	1

40

F	D	E	C	B	A
C	A	B	D	E	F
A	F	C	E	D	B
D	E	A	B	F	C
E	B	F	A	C	D
B	C	D	F	A	E

Solutions

41

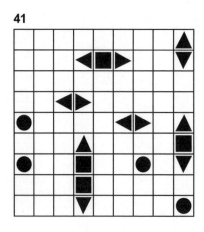

42

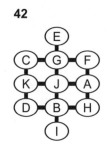

43

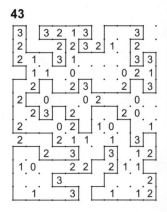

44

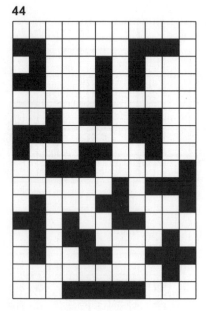

45

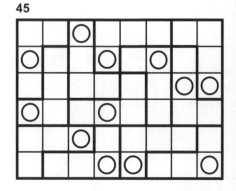

46

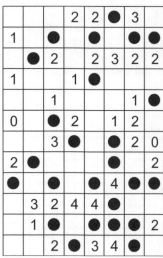

47
B

48
A4

49

3	4	4	2	2	1
1	3	3	2	2	4
1	3	3	2	2	4
4	4	4	3	3	2
4	4	4	3	3	2
1	2	2	3	3	1

50

F	E	B	C	D	A
A	B	F	D	C	E
E	A	D	F	B	C
D	C	E	A	F	B
C	F	A	B	E	D
B	D	C	E	A	F

Solutions

51

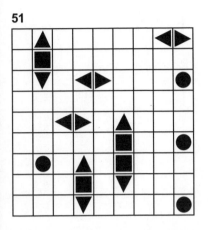

52

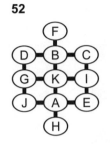

53

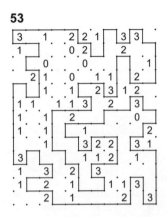

54

55

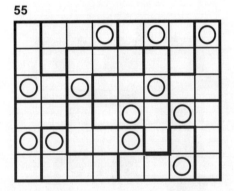

56

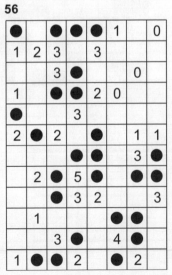

57
E

58
C4

59

1	3	3	2	2	3
1	3	3	4	4	4
1	3	3	4	4	4
4	2	2	2	2	1
4	2	2	2	2	1
2	1	1	3	3	4

60

E	A	B	D	F	C
D	F	A	C	E	B
B	C	D	F	A	E
A	E	F	B	C	D
F	B	C	E	D	A
C	D	E	A	B	F

195

Solutions

61

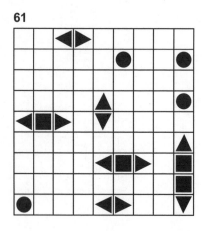

62

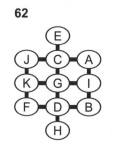

63

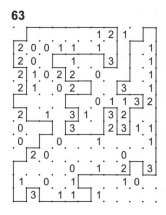

64

65

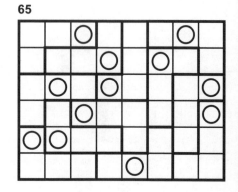

66

67
A

68
A3

69

3	3	3	4	4	3
3	2	2	1	1	3
3	2	2	1	1	3
1	2	2	4	4	4
1	2	2	4	4	4
1	4	4	3	3	4

70

C	E	A	B	F	D
D	F	C	A	B	E
F	B	E	D	C	A
A	D	B	C	E	F
E	C	D	F	A	B
B	A	F	E	D	C

Solutions

71

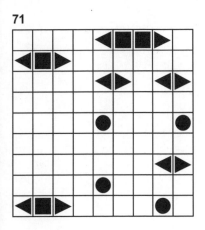

72

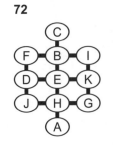

73

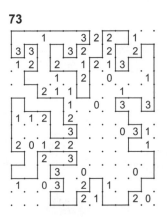

74

75

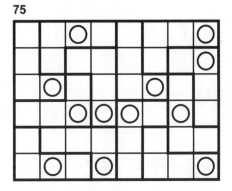

76

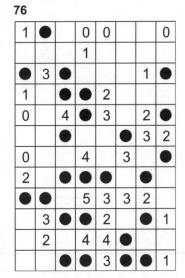

77
D

78
D6

79

4	4	4	2	2	2
3	1	1	2	2	2
3	1	1	2	2	2
2	3	3	1	1	4
2	3	3	1	1	4
3	4	4	3	3	2

80

E	C	F	B	A	D
A	D	C	F	E	B
B	E	A	C	D	F
D	F	B	A	C	E
F	A	D	E	B	C
C	B	E	D	F	A

Solutions

81

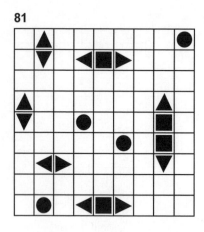

82

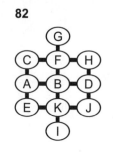

83

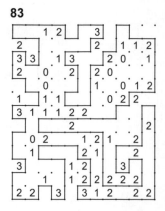

84

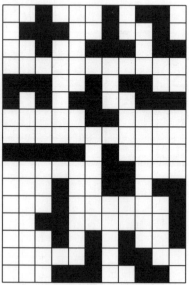

85

86

0		●	●	●	●	3	●
		●	4		●		
0					3		0
			3	●	●		
●		2	●	●	3		
	2	●	4		2		1
	3	4	●	1		●	
	●	●		1		1	
2	4	●			1	1	
●	3		●	2	1	●	
●		3	●				
2	●			2	●	1	

87
C

88
F6

89

3	3	3	2	2	4
2	2	2	1	1	3
2	2	2	1	1	3
4	3	3	1	1	4
4	3	3	1	1	4
3	4	4	1	1	4

90

A	B	C	F	E	D
C	E	F	D	B	A
B	D	E	A	C	F
E	F	D	B	A	C
D	A	B	C	F	E
F	C	A	E	D	B

Solutions

91

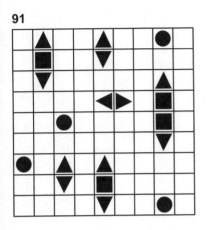

92

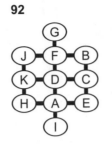

93

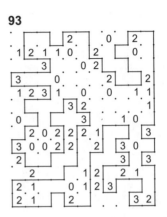

94

95

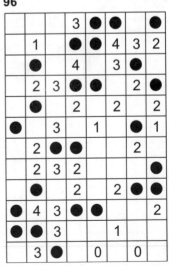

96

97
B

98
B3

99

2	2	2	4	4	1
4	1	1	1	1	4
4	1	1	1	1	4
3	4	4	4	4	4
3	4	4	4	4	4
1	1	1	3	3	2

100

C	D	A	E	B	F
F	A	B	D	C	E
B	E	C	A	F	D
E	C	D	F	A	B
A	F	E	B	D	C
D	B	F	C	E	A

199

Solutions

101

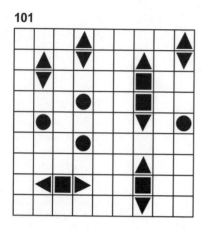

102

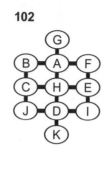

103

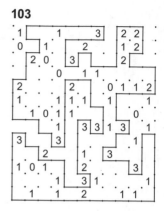

104

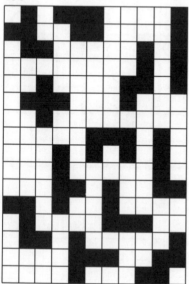

105

106

107
C

108
E4

109

4	2	2	2	2	4
3	4	4	2	2	1
3	4	4	2	2	1
1	3	3	3	3	2
1	3	3	3	3	2
1	4	4	4	4	1

110

D	E	B	C	A	F
F	A	E	D	C	B
C	B	D	A	F	E
B	D	C	F	E	A
A	C	F	E	B	D
E	F	A	B	D	C

Solutions

111

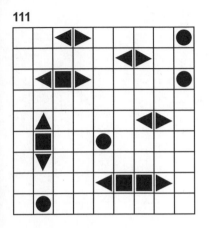

112

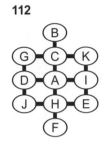

113

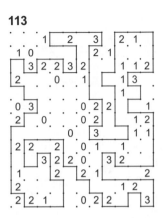

114

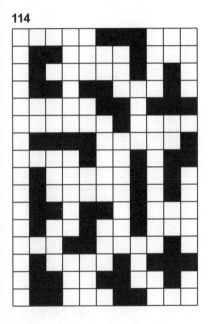

115

116

117
C

118
A4

119

4	2	2	4	4	1
3	2	2	3	3	3
3	2	2	3	3	3
1	3	3	4	4	2
1	3	3	4	4	2
1	2	2	1	1	1

120

C	F	E	D	B	A
A	B	C	E	D	F
D	A	B	F	E	C
B	E	F	C	A	D
E	C	D	A	F	B
F	D	A	B	C	E

Solutions

121

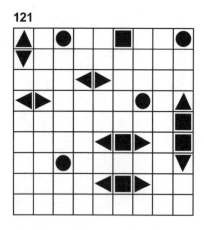

122

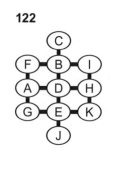

123

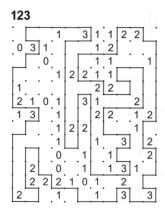

124

125

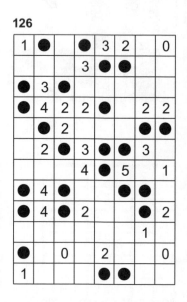

126

127
B

128
C7

129

1	4	4	3	3	4
2	1	1	1	1	4
2	1	1	1	1	4
2	3	3	1	1	2
2	3	3	1	1	2
4	3	3	2	2	1

130

A	D	F	E	C	B
C	F	B	D	E	A
B	C	E	A	D	F
D	A	C	B	F	E
E	B	D	F	A	C
F	E	A	C	B	D

Solutions

131

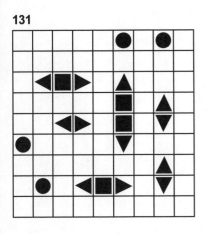

132

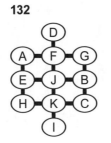

133

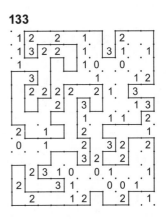

134

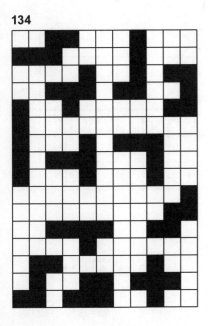

135

136

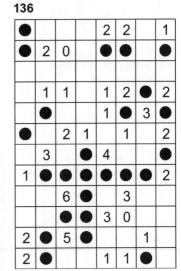

137

C

138

B5

139

2	2	2	3	3	2
1	3	3	1	1	1
1	3	3	1	1	1
3	4	4	4	4	2
3	4	4	4	4	2
1	4	4	3	3	2

140

D	C	F	E	B	A
E	D	C	A	F	B
F	B	E	D	A	C
A	E	B	C	D	F
C	F	A	B	E	D
B	A	D	F	C	E

Solutions

141

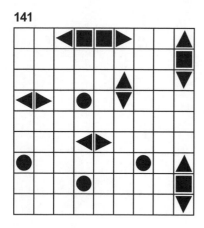

142

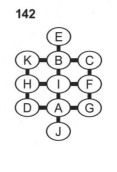

143

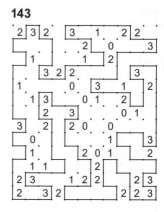

144

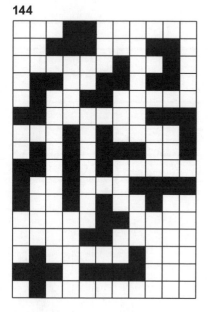

145

146

1		2		●	1		
	●	●	3				2
		3	3	●		●	●
0			●	3		●	3
	0		3	●		2	
		2	●	4	●		0
●	3		●				
3	●	●				●	1
●		●	2	2	●	4	●
	2	1			4	●	4
			1		●	●	●
	0	1	●			3	

147
B

148
D5

149

2	1	1	1	1	3
3	1	1	3	3	1
3	1	1	3	3	1
3	2	2	4	4	3
3	2	2	4	4	3
4	2	2	1	1	3

150

D	E	C	A	F	B
B	F	D	E	A	C
C	B	E	F	D	A
F	C	A	D	B	E
A	D	B	C	E	F
E	A	F	B	C	D

Solutions

151

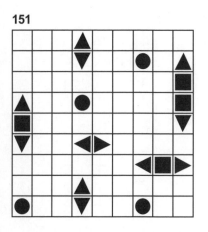

152

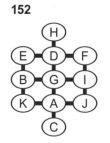

153

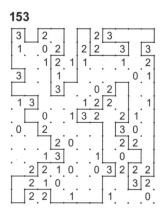

154

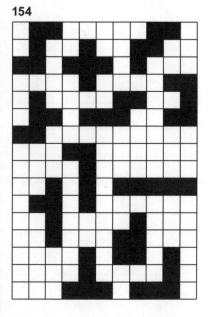

155

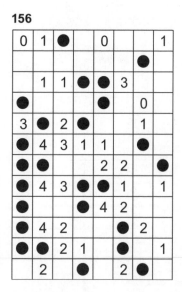

156

0	1	●		0			1
						●	
	1	1	●	●	3		
●				●		0	
3	●	2	●			1	
●	4	3	1	1		●	
●	●			2	2		●
●	4	3	●	●	1		1
●			●	4	2		
●	4	2			●	2	
●	●	2	1		●		1
	2		●		2	●	

157
D

158
F7

159

2	4	4	2	2	3
4	1	1	1	1	2
4	1	1	1	1	2
3	3	3	3	3	2
3	3	3	3	3	2
3	1	1	2	2	4

160

E	F	D	C	B	A
A	E	C	B	D	F
F	D	B	A	E	C
D	B	A	F	C	E
C	A	E	D	F	B
B	C	F	E	A	D

Solutions

161

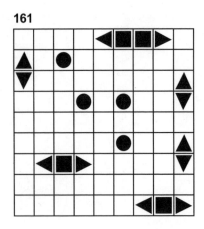

162

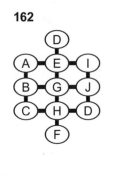

163

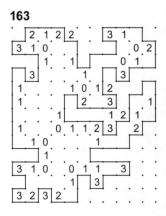

164

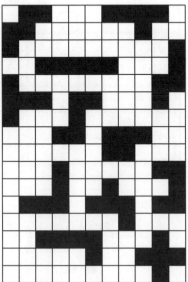

165

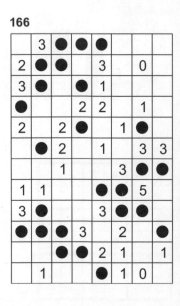

166

167
A

168
B7

169

2	2	2	3	3	4
1	3	3	4	4	3
1	3	3	4	4	3
3	2	2	4	4	1
3	2	2	4	4	1
3	3	3	3	3	1

170

A	E	B	D	C	F
E	C	A	F	D	B
F	B	C	E	A	D
B	D	E	C	F	A
D	A	F	B	E	C
C	F	D	A	B	E

Solutions

171

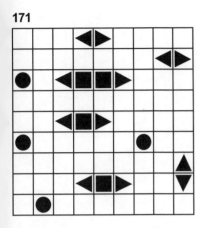

172

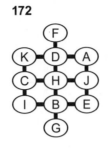

173

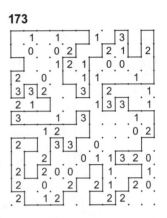

174

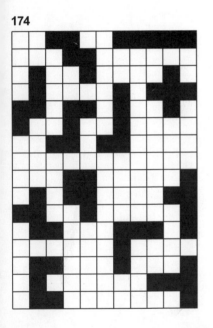

175

176

177

E

178

D3

179

1	1	1	4	4	4
2	2	2	1	1	3
2	2	2	1	1	3
1	3	3	4	4	1
1	3	3	4	4	1
3	4	4	2	2	4

180

E	D	B	F	C	A
B	A	C	D	F	E
D	E	F	A	B	C
F	B	A	C	E	D
A	C	E	B	D	F
C	F	D	E	A	B

Solutions

181

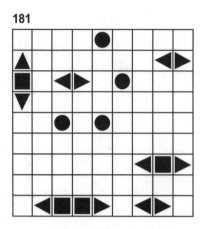

182

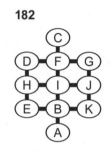

183

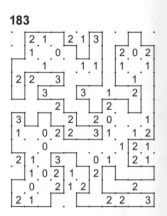

184

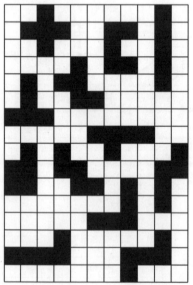